The Building Regulations 2000
As amended 2006

NON-DOMESTIC HEATING, COOLING AND VENTILATION COMPLIANCE GUIDE

COMPLIANCE WITH APPROVED DOCUMENTS
L2A: NEW BUILDINGS OTHER THAN DWELLINGS
AND L2B: EXISTING BUILDINGS OTHER
THAN DWELLINGS

First edition MAY 2006

London: TSO

Published by TSO (The Stationery Office) and available from:

Online
www.tsoshop.co.uk

Mail, Telephone, Fax & E-mail
TSO
PO Box 29, Norwich, NR3 1GN
Telephone orders/General enquiries: 0870 600 5522
Fax orders: 0870 600 5533
E-mail: customer.services@tso.co.uk
Textphone 0870 240 3701

TSO Shops
123 Kingsway, London WC2B 6PQ
020 7242 6393 Fax 020 7242 6394
66-69 Bull Street, Birmingham B4 6AD
0121 236 9596 Fax 0121 236 9699
9-21 Princess Street, Manchester M60 8AS
0161 834 7201 Fax 0161 833 0634
16 Arthur Street, Belfast BT1 4GD
028 9023 8451 Fax 028 9023 5401
18-19 High Street, Cardiff CF10 1PT
029 2039 5548 Fax 029 2038 4347
71 Lothian Road Edinburgh EH3 9AZ
0870 606 5566 Fax 0870 606 5588

TSO Accredited Agents
(see Yellow Pages)

and through good booksellers

First Published 2006

Crown copyright material is reproduced with the permission of the Controller of OPSI and the
Queen's Printer for Scotland.

Printed in Great Britain on material containing 75% post consumer and 25% mill broke.

ISBN 13   978-0-11-703648 2
ISBN 10   0-11-703648 X

N188029 C40 06/06

Contents

Section 1 Introduction

Part L of Schedule 1 to the Building Regulations[1] is concerned with the conservation of fuel and power in buildings. For buildings other than dwellings Part L is supported by two Approved Documents, Approved Document L2A (ADL2A) and Approved Document L2B (ADL2B). In addition to Part L, other Regulations also bear on the energy performance of buildings and their heating systems. ADL2A gives guidance on how to satisfy the energy performance provisions of the Building Regulations for new buildings. ADL2B gives guidance on how to satisfy the energy performance provisions of the Building Regulations for work in existing buildings. Both Approved Documents repeat the relevant regulatory requirements verbatim in various places distinguished by a green background with the aim of making them complete references for ordinary purposes. In cases of doubt however it may be necessary to refer direct to the Building Regulations as amended.

These Approved Documents were published in 2006 in support of the amendments to the Building Regulations, SI 2006/652. The amendment will come into force on 06 April 2006.

The revised Approved Documents, ADL2A and ADL2B, are more strategic in nature and rely on 'second-tier' documents to provide detailed information on how to comply with the requirements of Part L of the Regulations.

This guide (the 'Non-Domestic Heating, Cooling and Ventilation Compliance Guide') is a second-tier document referred to in ADL2A and ADL2B as a source of guidance on the means of complying with the requirements of Building Regulations Part L for space heating systems, hot water systems, cooling and ventilation systems. The guide was prepared by industry bodies and the Office of the Deputy Prime Minister (ODPM)*; it covers the conventional means of providing primary space heating, domestic hot water and comfort cooling and ventilation for buildings in use in England and Wales at the time of writing. When appropriate, the guide identifies the different requirements for systems in new build and those in existing buildings where work is being undertaken.

The guide outlines the minimum provisions for compliance with Part L for each type of heating, hot water, cooling or air distribution system as follows:

- The minimum provisions for efficiency of the plant that generates heat, hot water or cooling.

- The minimum provisions for controls to ensure that the system is not generating heat, hot water or cooling unnecessarily or excessively.

- A set of additional measures which may improve the efficiency of the plant; these are non-prescriptive and may be either required or optional depending on the type of plant.

- Minimum provisions for other factors affecting the safety or energy efficiency of the system.

- The minimum provision for insulation of pipes and ducts serving space heating, hot water and cooling systems.

- Minimum provisions for acceptable specific fan power ratings for fans serving air distribution systems.

The Building Regulations Part L now requires the energy performance of buildings other than dwellings to be calculated using the National Calculation Methodology (NCM)[2]. The NCM defines the procedure for calculating the annual energy use for a proposed building (based on a range of factors including the properties of the walls, floors, roofs and glazing as well as the building services) and comparing it with the energy use of a comparable 'notional' building. The NCM also calculates the rate of carbon emissions from the building which should not be greater than its Target Emission Rate as described in Approved Documents L and also calculated by the NCM. The NCM can be implemented through accredited simulation software or through the Simplified Building Energy Model (SBEM)[3].

---

*   On 5th May 2006 the responsibilities of the Office of the Deputy Prime Minister (ODPM) were passed to the Department for Communities and Local Government (DCLG).

[1]   The Building Regulations, SI 2006/652 including Part L of Schedule 1 apply in England and Wales. Separate Regulations apply in Scotland and Northern Ireland and may require different provisions from those signalled in this Guide as the minimum regulatory requirement.

[2]   The National Calculation Methodology for Part L, ODPM, 2006. ISBN 1 85946 227 8.

[3]   The Simplified Building Energy Model (SBEM) tool can be downloaded from www.odpm.gov.uk

This guide identifies the input parameters that are required by the accredited NCM models (e.g. SBEM), for space heating, hot water, comfort cooling and ventilation systems, in order to calculate the annual energy performance.

The key requirements for compliance with Part L and Approved Documents L2A and L2B and the key parameters for input into the accredited NCM models (e.g. SBEM) are summarised in a Compliance Checklist.

1.1 How to use this guide

This document provides guidance on the means of complying with the requirements of Building Regulations Part L for conventional space heating systems, hot water systems, cooling and ventilation systems in non-domestic buildings.

The guide addresses each technology in a separate section. These technology-specific sections are stand-alone but should be read alongside this introduction, and the generic sections that follow:

- Section 1.2 Definitions relevant to space heating and domestic hot water systems

- Section 1.3 Requirements of Approved Documents L2A and L2B

- Section 1.4 General guidance for compliance with ADL2A and ADL2B

- Section 10 Air distribution systems (if applicable)

- Section 11 Pipework and duct insulation

- Section 12 Compliance checklist and data input into the National Calculation Methodology tool

- Section 13 Glossary

The Non-domestic Heating, Cooling and Ventilation Compliance Guide identifies the minimum standards of provision that meet the requirements of Part L for systems in new build and those in existing buildings when work is being undertaken. The guide covers a range of frequently occurring situations but alternative means of achieving compliance may be possible. The status of alternative provisions is explained in the 'Use of Guidance' sections at the front of the Approved Documents.

Section 1.2 Definitions relevant to space heating and domestic hot water systems

The following generic definitions are used in this document. Specific definitions are also applicable to each type of heating plant or system depending on the relevant test procedures and are included in the relevant technology section of this guide.

It is important to note that this document deals only with the equipment that converts fuel or electricity to heat (the 'heat generator') and factors that improve the efficiency of the heat generator. Other aspects of the heat delivery system are addressed by the accredited NCM model (e.g. SBEM). Definitions relevant to cooling and ventilation systems are given in Section 9 and Section 10 of this guide, respectively.

Heat Generator – a device for converting fuel and/or electricity into heat, e.g. boiler, radiant heater.

Heat Generator Efficiency – Heat Generator Efficiency is the ratio of useful heat output to energy input in the fuel (based on gross calorific value) or electricity delivered to the heat generator as determined by the appropriate testing methods for that type of heat generator.

Heat Generator Seasonal Efficiency – the Heat Generator Seasonal Efficiency is the estimated seasonal ratio of heat input to heat output from the heat generator. This will depend on the Heat Generator Efficiency and the operating mode of the heat generator(s) over the heating season. For example, in the case of boilers it is a 'weighted' average of the efficiencies of the boiler at 30% and 100% of the boiler output. For other technologies the Heat Generator Seasonal Efficiency may be the same as the Heat Generator Efficiency.

Heating Efficiency Credits – these are awarded for the provision of specific measures. Different credits apply to measures possible for each of the heating or hot water technologies. Heating Efficiency Credits are added to the Heat Generator Seasonal Efficiency to obtain an Effective Heat Generating Seasonal Efficiency.

Effective Heat Generating Seasonal Efficiency – the Effective Heat Generating Seasonal Efficiency is calculated by adding the Heating Efficiency Credits, where applicable, to the Heat Generator Seasonal Efficiency as described in Equation 1. The Effective Heat Generating Seasonal Efficiency is the minimum efficiency that must be met by the heat generator and associated heating efficiency credits.

Effective Heat Generating Seasonal Efficiency =
Heat Generator Seasonal Efficiency + Heating Efficiency Credits   **Equation 1**

Minimum controls package – a package of controls specific to each technology that represents the minimum provision for controls to reduce carbon emissions from a space heating or hot water system. Heating Efficiency Credits are not available for the minimum controls package.

Additional controls and other measures – controls or other measures that go beyond the required minimum controls package and for which heating efficiency credits are available. For some types of heat generators (with an inherently low efficiency) the additional measures are required in order to achieve the minimum Effective Heat Generating Seasonal Efficiency.

Alternatively these additional measures can be used to exceed the required minimum performance level to improve the overall energy performance of the building.

Space heating system – the complete system that is installed to provide heating to the space. It includes the heating plant and the system by which the heating medium effects heating in the relevant zone. Heat losses from the distribution system can be addressed by reference to the TIMSA HVAC Insulation Guide[4].

Domestic hot water system – a local or central system for providing hot water for use by building occupants.

---

4   TIMSA HVAC Insulation Guide www.timsa.org.uk

Section 1.3 Requirements of Approved Documents L2A and L2B

The Building Regulations that bear on energy efficiency are repeated for easy reference at the front of both Approved Document L2A and Approved Document L2B before the sections giving technical guidance on compliance. The Approved Documents can be viewed on www.communities.gov.uk.

For new buildings the provision of heating and hot water services systems has to be considered as part of the overall design. For heating and hot water services systems, works in existing buildings provision can be considered in isolation. Both Approved Documents refer to this publication as the source of detailed guidance on what is reasonable provision.

This document is given as a source of guidance on showing compliance in paragraph 41 in Approved Document L2B.

Section 1.4 General guidance for compliance with L2A and L2B

Compliance with the Approved Documents, L2A and L2B, depends on meeting the minimum provisions for the following:

- *A minimum Heat Generator Seasonal Efficiency of the device that generates heat or hot water. The minimum Heat Generator Seasonal Efficiency for particular types of space heating and hot water systems is specified in Table 1. AND*

- *For heating and hot water systems, a minimum Effective Heat Generating Seasonal Efficiency as detailed in each technology-specific section of the guide. This will require the use of heating efficiency credits where the Heat Generator Seasonal Efficiency is less than the minimum requirement for the Effective Heat Generating Seasonal Efficiency. AND*

- *For cooling systems, a minimum Energy Efficiency Ratio as detailed in the cooling section of the guide. The minimum Energy Efficiency Ratio for particular types of cooling plant is specified in Table 1. AND*

- *A minimum controls package to ensure that the system is not generating heat, hot water or cooling unnecessarily or excessively. AND*

- *Additional measures which may improve the efficiency of the heat generator or cooling generator from a non-prescriptive list. This is necessary only for particular technologies. By providing additional measures heating plant efficiency credits can be gained. AND*

- *Insulation, to avoid excessive heat loss from pipes and ducts serving space heating or hot water systems, and to avoid heat gain by pipes and ducts serving cooling systems. AND*

- *An acceptable specific fan power for fans serving air distribution systems. The maximum permissible Specific Fan Power for particular types of air distribution systems is specified in Table 1. AND*

- *Other requirements for factors affecting the safety or energy efficiency of the system.*

Note that the minimum provision for the energy efficiency of heating plant is expressed in terms of the Effective Heat Generating Seasonal Efficiency. Recognition for exceeding the minimum provisions in new buildings is reflected in an improved energy performance rating when calculated in the accredited NCM tool. Similarly the Heat Generator Seasonal Efficiency and the minimum controls package both represent the minimum requirement for compliance with L2A and L2B.

Table 1 summarises the minimum provisions for the energy efficiency of the types of heating, hot water and cooling generator and ventilation systems covered by the Non-domestic Heating, Cooling and Ventilation Compliance Guide. Further guidance on how to comply with the values in Table 1 is given in the relevant technology sections that follow. Later sections of this document also describe the controls required for each type of heating, hot water or cooling system, additional controls and associated Heating Efficiency Credits and any other requirements.

Table 1 Minimum Heat Generator Seasonal Efficiency for primary heating systems, hot water systems, minimum Energy Efficiency Ratios for cooling systems and maximum permissible specific fan powers for air distribution systems

Primary space heating system	System type	Required Minimum Boiler Seasonal Efficiency (based on gross calorific value)
Boilers in new build	Natural gas	Single boiler system – 0.84 Multiple-boiler system – 0.80 for any individual boiler and 0.84 for the overall multi-boiler system
	LPG	Single boiler system – 0.84 Multiple-boiler system – 0.80 for any individual boiler and 0.84 for the overall multi-boiler system
	Oil	Single boiler system – 0.84 Multiple-boiler system – 0.80 for any individual boiler and 0.84 for the overall multi-boiler system
Boilers in existing buildings	Natural gas	80%
	LPG	81%
	Oil	82%
Gas and oil-fired warm air systems		**Required minimum thermal efficiency (based on gross calorific value)**
	Gas-fired forced convection heater without a fan complying with EN 621	80%
	Fan assisted gas-fired forced convection complying with EN 1020	80%
	Direct gas-fired forced convection heater complying with EN 525	90%
	Oil fired forced convection	80%
Radiant heaters	Luminous (unflued)	85.5%
	Non-luminous (unflued)	85.5%
	Non-luminous flued	73.8%
	Multi-burner radiant heaters	80%
Heat pumps		**Required Minimum Heating CoP (at design condition)**
	All types except absorption heat pumps and gas engine heat pumps	2.0
	Absorption heat pumps	0.5
	Gas engine driven heat pumps	1.0
CHP		**Required Minimum CHPQA Quality Index (CHPQA QI)**
	All types	105
Electric (primary) heating	Boiler	N/A
	Warm air	N/A

Domestic hot water systems		Required minimum thermal efficiencies (based on gross calorific value)
Direct-fired	Natural gas	73%
	LPG-fired	74%
	Oil-fired	75%
Indirect-fired (dedicated hot water boiler)	Natural gas	80%
	LPG-fired	81%
	Oil-fired	82%
Electric DHW heaters		N/A
Comfort cooling systems		**Required minimum Energy Efficiency Ratio (EER)**
	Packaged air conditioners – single duct types	1.8
	Packaged air conditioners – other types	2.2
	Split and multi-split air conditioners (including VRF)	2.4
	Vapour compression cycle chillers – water cooled	3.4
	Vapour compression cycle chillers – air cooled	2.25
	Water loop heat pump	3.2
	Absorption cycle chillers	0.5
	Gas fired Variable Refrigerant Flow (VRF)	1.0
Air distribution systems		**Maximum permissible specific fan power (Watts/(litre/s))**
New buildings	Central mechanical ventilation including heating, cooling and heat recovery	2.5
	Central mechanical ventilation with heating and cooling	2.0
	All other central systems	1.8
	Local ventilation only units within the local area, such as window/wall/roof units, serving one room or area	0.5
	Local ventilation only units remote from the area such as ceiling void or roof mounted units, serving one room or area	1.2
	Other local units, e.g. fan coil units (rating weighted average)	0.8

Existing buildings	Central mechanical ventilation including heating, cooling and heat recovery	3.0
	Central mechanical ventilation with heating and cooling	2.5
	All other central systems	2.0
	Local ventilation only units within the local area, such as window/wall/roof units, serving one room or area	0.5
	Local ventilation only units remote from the area such as ceiling void or roof mounted units, serving one room or area	1.5
	Other local units, e.g. fan coil units (rating weighted average)	0.8

Section 2 Gas and oil-fired boilers

2.1 Introduction

This section outlines the minimum provisions needed to comply with Part L when space heating in new build and in existing buildings is provided by boiler systems. It addresses the relevant boiler types and measures, such as controls, for which the associated energy efficiency benefits may be added to the Heat Generator Seasonal Efficiency.

2.2 Scope of the guidance

The guidance given here applies to commercial boilers for use in wet central heating systems as follows:

- Natural gas boilers.
- Liquid petroleum gas (LPG) boilers.
- Oil-fired boilers.

It does not cover the use of:

- Steam boilers (these are used primarily for processes rather than the provision of space heating).
- Electric boilers (see Section 7 of this document for guidance on electric heating).

2.3 Definitions

The terminology used to describe efficiencies for boiler systems is detailed below. In this section a heat generator refers to a boiler.

Boiler Efficiency – the energy delivered by the water as it leaves the boiler (or boilers in multi-boiler installations) to supply the heat emitters divided by the energy (based on gross calorific value) in the fuel delivered to the boiler expressed as a percentage. It is an expression of the boiler performance and excludes boiler and auxiliary controls energy, pumps, boiler room ventilation fans, mechanical flue extraction fans and fan dilution systems.

The boiler efficiency is measured according to the standards that are used to demonstrate compliance with the Boiler Efficiency Directive[5].

Economiser – a device including a secondary heat exchanger fitted on, or near to, a boiler providing additional heat transfer capacity. For the purpose of this guide, any boiler which will be supplied with an economiser should have the economiser fitted when the boiler efficiency is tested according to the standards that are used to demonstrate compliance with the Boiler Efficiency Directive if the efficiency benefits of the economiser are to be included in the calculation of Boiler Efficiency using Equation 2, 3.1, or 3.2 and 3.3 (as appropriate).

2.4 Determining Seasonal Boiler Efficiency

Seasonal Boiler Efficiency for single boiler systems and multiple-boiler systems using identical boilers – for boilers the relevant heat generator seasonal efficiency is the seasonal boiler efficiency. The Seasonal Boiler Efficiency is a 'weighted' average of the efficiencies of the boiler at 15%, 30% and 100% of the boiler output (the efficiency at 15% is taken to be the same as that at 30%). This is usually quoted by the boiler manufacturer. Note that the efficiency based on net calorific value should be converted to that based on gross calorific value using the appropriate conversion factor in Appendix 1.

---

[5] Council Directive 92/42/EEC (the Boiler Efficiency Directive) relates to the efficiency requirements for new hot water boilers fired with liquid or gaseous fuels. The associated UK legislation is the Boiler (Efficiency) Regulations 1993 (SI 1993/3083), amended by the Boiler (Efficiency) (Amendment) Regulations 1994 (SI 1994/3083).

The Boiler Efficiencies, measured at 100% load and at 30%, are used as the basis for calculating the Seasonal Boiler Efficiency as described by Equation 2. The weighting factors given in Equation 2 should be used as they represent typical seasonal operating conditions for the boiler.

Equation 2 applies in the following conditions:

- single boiler systems where the boiler output is ≤ 400kW and the boiler will operate on a low temperature system;

- multiple-boiler systems where all individual boilers have identical efficiencies AND where the output of each boiler is ≤ 400kW operating on low temperature systems.

For boilers with an output > 400kW the manufacturer's declared efficiencies should be used.

Seasonal Boiler Efficiency **Equation 2[6]**
$$= 0.81\,\eta_{30\%} + 0.19\,\eta_{100\%}$$

where the terms in Equation 2 are defined as follows:

- $\eta_{30\%}$% is the gross boiler efficiency measured at 30% load;
- $\eta_{100\%}$% is the gross boiler efficiency measured at 100% load.

Seasonal Boiler Efficiency for a multiple-boiler system replacing an existing installation where the component boilers have non-identical efficiencies – where more than one boiler is installed on the same heating system and the efficiencies of the boilers are not all identical, Equation 3.1 should be used to calculate the overall Seasonal Boiler Efficiency. All boilers should be included in the calculation, even when some are identical.

Seasonal Boiler Efficiency (multiple-boiler **Equation 3.1**
systems with non-identical boilers)
$$= \eta_{OSBE} = \frac{\eta_{SBE}.R}{\sum R}$$

where the terms in Equation 3.1 are defined as follows:

- η_{OSBE} is the gross overall seasonal boiler efficiency, being a weighted average with respect to boiler output, of the individual seasonal boiler efficiencies;
- η_{SBE} is the gross seasonal boiler efficiency of each individual boiler calculated using Equation 2;
- R is the rated output in kW of each individual boiler (at 80ºC/60ºC).

Seasonal Boiler Efficiency for a multi-boiler system in a new building – in the case of multiple boilers in new build, the more accurate three-step method described below should be used to calculate the overall seasonal boiler efficiency for multiple-boilers. These steps can readily be programmed into a spreadsheet to automate the calculation.

Step 1

Determine which boilers are operating at what individual part load level at each of the three system part load conditions of 15%, 30% and 100%. For example, if the total system output is made up of three equally sized boilers, at 15% of system output, the lead boiler will be operating at 45% of its rated output, with the other two boilers switched off.

Step 2

Determine the efficiency at which each individual boiler is operating at each of the above operating conditions. In the above example, the efficiency of the boiler operating at 45% can be determined by linear interpolation between its efficiencies at 30% and 100% of rated output. Where it is necessary to determine the efficiency of an individual boiler at 15% of rated output, this should be taken as the same as the efficiency at 30% of rated output. (Note that the efficiency at 15% of rated output will only be needed if a single boiler meets the full design output.)

---

6   This equation assumes that the efficiency at 15% load is taken to be the same as that at 30% (and therefore the equation has been simplified accordingly).

Step 3

Calculate the overall operating efficiency at each of the system part load conditions. This is calculated by the following formula:

$$\eta_p = \frac{Q_p}{\sum \dfrac{q_{b,p}}{\eta_{b,p}}}$$

Equation 3.2

where

η_p = the system efficiency at part load condition p, i.e. 15%, 30% and 100% of system rated output.
Q_p = the system heat output at part load condition p.
$q_{b,p}$ = the individual boiler heat output at system part load condition p.
$\eta_{b,p}$ = the individual boiler efficiency at system part load condition p.

Calculate the overall seasonal boiler efficiency as the weighted average of the efficiencies at the three load conditions using the following equation:

Equation 3.3

$$\eta_{OSBE} = 0.36\,\eta_{p=15\%} + 0.45\,\eta_{p=30\%} + 0.19\,\eta_{p=100\%}$$

Table 2 is a worksheet that can be used to follow through these calculations. Table 3 shows a completed example calculation using this worksheet, for the case where a system with a rated output of 600kW is served by three boilers, each rated at 250kW. The first two boilers are condensing boilers, with the third being a standard boiler. Because the installation is oversized (750kW compared to 600kW), even at full system output, the final boiler is only operating at 40% output (100/250).

The notes at the foot of Table 3 illustrate how the various values are calculated.

Table 2 Worksheet for calculating the overall seasonal boiler efficiency of a multiple-boiler system using the alternative three-step method

Boiler no.	Rating kW	Efficiency at stated % of boiler output		Boiler output at stated % of system output			Boiler efficiency at stated % of system output		
		@100%	@30%	15%	30%	100%	15%	30%	100%
1									
2									
3									
4									
5									
6									
7									
8									
System efficiency at part load									
Weighting factor							0.36	0.45	0.19
Overall seasonal boiler efficiency									

Table 3 Example calculation of the overall seasonal boiler efficiency of a multiple boiler system in a new building

Boiler no.	Rating kW	Efficiency at stated % of boiler output		Boiler output at stated % of system output			Boiler efficiency at stated % of system output		
		@100%	@30%	15%	30%	100%	15%	30%	100%
1	250	86.0	90.0	36.0%	72.0%	100.0%	89.66%[1]	87.60%	86.00%
2	250	86.0	90.0	0.0%	0.0%	100.0%	90.00%	90.00%	86.00%
3	250	85.0	85.0	0.0%	0.0%	40.0%	77.00%	77.00%	85.00%
System efficiency at part load							89.66%	87.60%	85.41%[2]
Weighting factor							0.36	0.45	0.19
Overall seasonal boiler efficiency							87.28%[3]		

Notes

1: calculated by linear interpolation

$$\eta_{1,30\%} = \eta_{30\%} + (\eta_{30\%} - \eta_{100\%}) * \frac{(36\% - 30\%)}{(100\% - 30\%)}$$

2: calculated by dividing the thermal output of the system (600kW) by the rate of fuel consumption, which is given by the sum of the boiler outputs divided by their individual operating efficiency, i.e.

$$600 / \left[\frac{250*100\%}{86.00\%} + \frac{250*100\%}{86.00\%} + \frac{250*40\%}{85.00\%} \right] = 85.41\%$$

3: calculated as the weighted average, i.e. 89.66%*0.36 + 87.60%*0.45 + 85.41%*0.19 = 87.92%

Effective Heat Generating Seasonal Efficiency – this is equivalent to the heat generator seasonal efficiency, that is the Boiler Seasonal Efficiency (as calculated by Equation 2 for individual boilers or by Equation 3.1) plus any heating efficiency credits that apply for existing installations.

Economisers – where the boiler manufacturer supplies an economiser as part of the boiler (as a matched package) and the combined unit is tested to the standards needed to demonstrate compliance with the Boiler Efficiency Directive, the effect of this on the boiler efficiency at 30% and 100% of the boiler output may be taken into account in the values used for the calculation of the Heat Generator Seasonal Efficiency (Seasonal Boiler Efficiency) using Equations 2 or 3.1 or the three-step method and Equations 3.2 and 3.3, as appropriate.

2.5 Boilers in new buildings

Background

It is essential that any new building will be provided with high efficiency condensing and/or non-condensing boilers and the minimum provisions with respect to the heat generator seasonal efficiency reflect this requirement.

Commercial heating systems are inherently more complicated than domestic systems with a wider range of temperatures and heat emitters. The selection of condensing or non-condensing boilers will therefore need to be determined by application and physical restraints.

Condensing boilers will meet projected efficiencies only when they operate with a system return temperature between 30°C and 40°C for 80% of the annual operating hours. With a return temperature of 55°C and above, condensing boilers will not produce condensate and will have similar efficiencies to non-condensing high efficiency boilers. Some systems are suitable for outside compensator control that allows return temperatures to fall into the condensing range for some periods of the heating season and these may be best served by a mixture of condensing and non-condensing boilers.

In the case of boilers in new buildings the minimum Heat Generator Seasonal Efficiency is equivalent to the minimum Effective Heat Generating Seasonal Efficiency.

Minimum provisions for boilers in new buildings

In order to comply with ADL2A, when installing boiler plant in new buildings the following minimum provisions should be met:

a.   Where a single boiler is used to meet the heat demand, the boiler should achieve a boiler seasonal efficiency (gross calorific value) as given in Equation 2, of not less than 84%; OR

b.   For multiple-boiler systems, each boiler should have a boiler seasonal efficiency of not less than 80% (gross calorific value) as defined by Equation 2; AND the overall boiler seasonal efficiency of the multi-boiler system, as defined by Equation 3.1 for an existing installation or the three-step method and Equations 3.2 and 3.3 for new building installations, should be no less than 84%; AND

c.   The relevant minimum controls package in Table 4 should be adopted.

Table 4 Minimum controls package for new boilers or multiple-boiler systems (depending on boiler plant output or combined boiler plant output)

Boiler plant output	Minimum controls package	Minimum controls package
<100kW	A	• Timing and temperature demand control which should be zone-specific where the building floor area is greater than 150m²
		• Weather compensation except where a constant temperature supply is required
100kW to 500kW	B	• Controls package A above PLUS
		• Optimal start/stop control is required with night set-back OR frost protection outside occupied periods
		• Boiler with two stage high/low firing facility or multiple boilers should be installed to provide efficient part-load performance
		For multiple boilers, sequence control should be provided AND boilers, by design or application, should have limited heat loss from non-firing modules, for example by using isolation valves or dampers. For boilers with low standing losses isolation valves and dampers would not be required
		Individual boilers, by design or application, should have limited heat loss from non-firing modules, for example by using isolation valves or dampers.
>500kW – individual boilers	C	• Controls package A above AND Controls package B PLUS:
		• The burner controls should be fully modulating for gas-fired boilers or multi-stage for oil-fired boilers

The correct efficiency to input into the accredited NCM tool when calculating the energy performance rating is the effective heat-generating seasonal efficiency. For boilers in new buildings there are no Heating Efficiency Credits available and the Effective Heat Generating Seasonal Efficiency is therefore the same as the Heat Generator Seasonal Efficiency.

2.6 Boilers in existing buildings

Background

Boiler efficiencies have improved markedly over recent years. A boiler meeting the minimum required efficiency in 1989 would have a Boiler Seasonal Efficiency of approximately 65%, whereas a boiler meeting the minimum requirements of the Boiler Efficiency Directive would have a Boiler Seasonal Efficiency of approximately 78.5% (both based on gross calorific value). This improvement in boiler efficiency represents an energy saving of approximately 17%.

This guidance recognises that in many cases using condensing boiler technology in existing buildings would be either technically impractical (because of flueing constraints) or economically unviable. For this reason non-condensing boilers may be used provided that the minimum provisions for efficiency are met as given in this section.

Minimum provisions for replacement boilers

In order to comply with ADL2B, when installing boiler plant in existing buildings the following minimum provisions should be met:

a.   Each boiler (regardless of whether it is in a single-boiler system or part of a multiple-boiler system) should have a minimum Boiler Seasonal Efficiency (gross calorific value), as calculated by Equation 2, no worse than the relevant value in Table 5;

b.   For multiple-boiler systems the minimum seasonal boiler efficiency as determined by Equation 3.1 should be no worse than the relevant value in Table 5;

AND

c.   A minimum controls package should be adopted as described in Table 6;

AND

d.   The Effective Heat Generating Seasonal Efficiency should be no less than the relevant value in Table 5. Additional measures from Table 7 must be adopted to gain Heating Efficiency Credits if the Boiler Seasonal Efficiency is less than the relevant value of the Effective Heat Generating Seasonal Efficiency.

Table 5 Required Minimum Effective Heat Generating Seasonal Efficiencies and minimum boiler seasonal efficiency for boiler systems in existing buildings

Fuel type	Minimum Effective Heat Generating Seasonal Efficiency (% gross calorific value)	Minimum Boiler Seasonal Efficiency (% gross calorific value)
Gas (Natural)	84	80
Gas (LPG)	85	81
Oil	86	82

Table 6 Minimum controls package for replacement boilers in existing buildings

Minimum controls package for replacement boilers	Suitable controls
Zone controls	Zone control is required only for buildings where the floor area is greater than 150m^2. As a minimum, on/off control (e.g. through an isolation valve for unoccupied zones) should be provided. This is achieved by default for a building of floor area 150m^2 or less
Demand controls	Room thermostat which controls through a diverter valve with constant boiler flow water temperature. This method of control is not suitable for condensing boilers
Time controls	Time clock controls

Heating Efficiency Credits for replacement boilers

Where the Boiler Seasonal Efficiency is less than the minimum Effective Heat Generating Efficiency for that type of boiler, additional measures must be adopted in order to achieve a minimum Effective Heat Generating Seasonal Efficiency of not less than the relevant value in Table 5. Table 7 indicates the range of additional measures which may be adopted and the relevant efficiency credit that is applicable.

Table 7 Heating Efficiency Credits for measures applicable to boiler replacement in existing buildings

Measure		Heating efficiency credits % points	Comments/definition
A	Boiler oversize ≤ 20%	2	Boiler oversize is defined as the amount by which the *maximum boiler heat output* exceeds heat output of the system at design conditions, expressed as a percentage of the system heat output. For multiple-boiler systems the *maximum boiler heat output* is the sum of the maximum outputs of all the boilers in the system.

B	Multiple boilers	1	Where more than one boiler is used to meet the heat load.
C	Sequential control of multiple-boiler systems	1	Applies only to multi-boiler/module arrangements. It is recommended that the most efficient boiler(s) should act as the lead in a multi-boiler system.
D	Monitoring and targeting	1	Means of identifying changes in operation or onset of faults. The credit can only be claimed if metering is included and a scheme for data collection is provided and available for inspection.
E	i) Thermostatic Radiator Valves (TRV) alone. Would also apply to fanned convector systems	1	TRVs enable the building temperature to be controlled and therefore reduce waste of energy.
	ii) Weather (inside/outside temperature) compensation system using a mixing valve	1.5	Provides more accurate prediction of load and hence control.
	iii) Addition of TRV or temperature zone control to (ii) above to ensure full building temperature control	1	This credit is additional to E (ii) above.
F	i) A 'room' thermostat or sensor that controls boiler water temperature in relation to heat load	0.5	
	ii) Weather (inside/outside temperature) compensation system that is direct acting	2	Provides more accurate prediction of load and hence control.
	iii) Addition of TRV or temperature zone control to (i) or (ii) above to ensure full building temperature control	1	This credit is additional to F (i) or F (ii) above. Note F (i) and F (ii) are not used together.
G	i) Optimised start	1.5	A control system which starts plant operation at the latest time possible to achieve specified conditions at the start of the occupancy period.
	ii) Optimised stop	0.5	A control system which stops plant operation at the earliest possible time such that internal conditions will not deteriorate beyond preset limits by the end of the occupancy period.
	iii) Optimised start/stop	2	A control system which starts plant operation at the latest time possible to achieve specified conditions at the start of the occupancy period and stops plant operation at the earliest possible time such that internal conditions will not deteriorate beyond preset limits by the end of the occupancy period. Note that if optimised start/stop systems are installed credits G (i) and G (ii) cannot also be claimed.
H	Full zoned time control	1	Allowing each zone to operate independently in terms of start/stop time. Only applicable where operational conditions change in different zones. Does not include local temperature control.

I	Full building management system (BMS)	4	A full BMS will allow control, with respect to the heating plant, of the following: the sequential control of multiple boilers, full zoned time controls and weather compensation where applicable; frost protection and/or night set-back; optimisation and monitoring and targeting.
			Note that if a full BMS is installed, where credits are available for the individual components of a full BMS, the credits for the components can not be claimed in addition to these 4 percentage points. So, for example where a full BMS was installed that allowed sequential control of multiple boilers, credit C could not be claimed in addition to credit I.
J	Decentralised heating systems	1	Elimination of long pipe runs between buildings or through unheated areas in existing systems in order to reduce excessive heat losses.

Example 1: Using Heating Efficiency Credits to achieve the minimum Effective Heat Generating Seasonal Efficiency for a boiler system in an existing building

An existing boiler will be replaced with a gas boiler with a seasonal efficiency of the minimum 80% allowed for this boiler type.

To achieve the minimum Effective Heat Generating Seasonal Efficiency of at least 84%, additional measures, with associated Heating Efficiency Credits, must be adopted.

The following approach would achieve this:

- A decision has been made to restrict oversizing to 15% (after a detailed assessment of load).

- Two equally sized boilers will be used to meet the heat load in place of the existing single boiler.

- TRVs will be fitted to control the temperature in areas other than where the 'room thermostat' is fitted.

- The boilers will be fired by natural gas.

Table 8 below shows how credits would be awarded in this example:

Table 8 Example to illustrate allocation of Heating Efficiency Credits for a replacement boiler in an existing building

Plant description	Heating efficiency credits (% points)
Boiler efficiency	80%
Boiler oversizing is less than 20%	2
System controlled by room thermostat which controls boiler water temperature	0.5
System uses TRVs to ensure full building temperature control	1
Multiple boilers	1
Total credits	**4.5**

From Equation 1 (Section 1.2): Effective Heat Generating Seasonal Efficiency = (Boiler Seasonal Efficiency) + Total Heating Efficiency Credits

= 80% + 4.5% = 84.5%

In this example the minimum requirement of an effective heat-generating seasonal efficiency of 84% is exceeded by 0.5%.

2.7 Glossary of boiler terminology

Condensing boilers

Condensing boilers offer higher energy efficiencies by recovering heat from the flue gases. This is achieved by increasing the heat exchanger surface area which recovers extra sensible heat whenever the boiler fires. They become even more efficient when system water temperatures are low because the extra heat exchanger promotes condensation, allowing much of the latent heat to be recaptured. Standing losses (when the boiler is not firing) are low and part load performance is very good. In multiple-boiler systems condensing boilers can be used as the lead boiler.

Standard boiler

In the context of this document, a standard boiler denotes a boiler that is non-condensing.

Zone control

Rooms or areas within buildings may need to be heated to different temperatures and/or at different times, each requiring independent control. Where several rooms or areas of a building behave in a similar manner, they can be grouped together as a 'zone' and put on the same circuit and controller.

Sequence control

This enables two or more heating boilers to be controlled in order to achieve the desired heat output temperature. This maximises the efficiency of the boilers by switching them off in sequence when the heating load declines. This reduces fuel consumption as well as wear and tear on the boilers.

Direct acting weather compensation

These controls enable a condensing boiler to work at its optimum efficiency. The controls allow the boiler to vary its operating flow temperature automatically, to suit weather conditions and the temperatures inside the building. Weather compensation relies on communication between an external sensor and one inside the boiler. The boiler's water flow temperature is varied accordingly, rather than the boiler turning on and off which wastes energy.

Weather compensation via a mixing valve

Similar to 'Direct acting weather compensation' except that the temperature of water supplied to the heat emitters is controlled by mixing the boiler flow and return instead of by altering the boiler temperature.

Optimiser

A control system employing an optimum start algorithm.

Optimum start

A control system or algorithm which starts plant operation at the latest time possible to achieve specified conditions at the start of the occupancy period.

Optimum stop

A control system or algorithm which stops plant operation at the earliest possible time such that internal conditions will not deteriorate beyond preset limits by the end of the occupancy period.

Two-stage burner control – two-stage burner control enables two distinct firing rates.

Multi-stage burner control – multi-stage burner control will allow more than two distinct firing rates but without continuous adjustment between firing rates.

Modulating burner control – having continuous adjustment between firing rates. Modulating burner control will alter the firing rate to match the boiler load over the whole turndown ratio.

Decentralisation

The replacement of centralised boiler plant and its associated distribution pipework with several smaller, more accurately sized boiler plants, installed within or adjacent to the buildings or systems they serve. This enables elimination of long pipe runs between buildings or through unheated areas in existing systems in order to reduce excessive heat losses.

Building Management System (BMS)

A building-wide network which allows communication with and control of items of HVAC plant (and other building systems) from a single remote control centre.

Full Building Management System

A full Building Management System will include, with respect to the heating plant, the sequential control of multiple boilers, full zone controls and compensation where applicable; frost protect and/or night set-back; optimisation and monitoring and targeting.

Section 3 Heat pumps

3.1 Introduction

This section outlines the minimum provisions needed to comply with Part L when space heating in new build and in existing buildings is provided by heating-only heat pumps or reverse cycle heat pumps.

It addresses the relevant heat pump types and measures, such as controls, for which the associated energy efficiency benefits may be added to the Heat Generator Seasonal Efficiency. For these purposes a heat pump is a device which takes heat energy from a low temperature source and upgrades it to a higher temperature at which it can be usefully employed for heating.

For guidance on heat pumps that also provide cooling see Section 9 of this guide.

3.2 Scope of the guidance

The guidance in this section applies to commercial heat pump systems as outlined in Table 9. Table 9 categorises the different types of heat pump depending on the source of the heat; the medium to which it is delivered; and the technology of the system.

Table 9 Heat pump types and associated test standards

Heat pump type	Technology	Sub-technology	Test standard
Electrically driven warm air heat pump systems	Ground to air	Single package	ISO 13256-1[8]
		Energy transfer systems (matching heating/cooling demands in buildings)	
	Water to air	Single package	BS EN 14511[9]
		Energy transfer systems (matching heating/cooling demands in buildings)	
	Air to air	Single package	BS EN 14511
		Split system	
		Multi-split system	
		Variable refrigerant flow systems	
Electrically-driven warm water systems	Ground to water	Single package	ISO 13256-2[10]
		Split package	
	Water to water	Single package	BS EN 14511
		Split package	
	Air to water	Single package	BS EN 14511
		Split package	
Gas-engine driven	Available as variable refrigerant flow warm air systems		Generally to BS EN 14511

3.3 Definitions

Coefficient of Performance (CoP)

For heat pumps the efficiency is defined in terms of the Coefficient of Performance (CoP). This is a measure of the heating efficiency of heat pumps and may also be expressed as a percentage.

---

[8] ISO 13256-1 Water-source heat pumps – Testing and rating for performance – Part 1: Water-to-air and brine-to-air heat pumps.

[9] BS EN 14511 (2004) Air conditioners, liquid chilling packages and heat pumps with electrically driven compressors for space heating and cooling. Test conditions.

[10] ISO 13256-2 Water-source heat pumps – Testing and rating for performance – Part 2: Water-to-water and brine-to-water heat pumps.

The heating CoP for a heat pump is the heat output of the heat pump divided by its power input as in Equation 4.

Heating CoP (%) = (Heat output/power input) x 100 **Equation 4**

In order to calculate the CoP the heat pump should be tested in line with the relevant standard for the technology in Table 9. The input power items that should be incorporated in this calculation are defined in the relevant test standard.

3.4 Minimum provisions for heat pumps in new and existing buildings

In order to comply with ADL2A and ADL2B, for heat pump systems in new and existing buildings, the following minimum provisions should be met:

a.   The heat pump system should achieve a minimum Coefficient of Performance (Heat Generator Seasonal Efficiency) no worse than the applicable value in Table 10;

AND

b.   A minimum controls package should be adopted as detailed in Table 11.

There are currently no test standards in the EU for part load testing of heat pumps so a single minimum figure should be used that must be achieved at the heating system design conditions.

Table 10 Required minimum CoPs (Heat Generator Efficiencies) for heat pumps systems in new and existing buildings

Heat pump type	Heating CoP Heat Generator Efficiency (%)
All types (except absorption heat pumps and gas-engine heat pumps)	2.0 (200%) when operating at the design conditions
Absorption heat pumps	0.5 (50%) when operating at the design conditions
Gas-engine heat pumps	1.0 (100%) when operating at the design conditions

The minimum provisions for controls given in Table 11 should be provided. Heating efficiency credits are not available for these control measures.

Table 11 Minimum controls package for heat pump systems in new and existing buildings

Heat source/ sink	Technology	Minimum controls package	Minimum controls package
All types	All technologies	A	On/off zone control. If the unit serves a single zone, and for buildings with a floor area of 150m² or less, the minimum requirement is achieved by default Time control
Air to air	Single package	B	Controls package A above PLUS Heat pump unit controls to include: Control of room air temperature (if not provided externally) Control of outdoor fan operation Defrost control of external airside heat exchanger Control for secondary heating (if fitted) External controls should include: Room thermostat (if not provided internal to the HP) to regulate the space temperature and interlocked with the heat pump unit operation

	Split system Multi-split system Variable refrigerant flow system	B	Controls package A above PLUS Heat pump unit controls to include: Control of room air temperature (if not provided externally) Control of outdoor fan operation Defrost control of external airside heat exchanger Control for secondary heating (if fitted) External controls should include: Room thermostat (if not provided internal to the HP) to regulate the space temperature and interlocked with the heat pump unit operation
Water or ground to air	Single package energy transfer systems (matching heating/cooling demand in buildings)	D	Controls package A above PLUS Heat pump unit controls to include: Control of room air temperature (if not provided externally) Control of outdoor fan operation for cooling tower or dry cooler (energy transfer systems) Control for secondary heating (if fitted) on air to air systems Control of external water pump operation External controls should include: Room thermostat (if not provided internal to the HP) to regulate the space temperature and interlocked with the heat pump system operation
Air to water Water or ground to water	Single package Split package	E	Controls package A above PLUS Heat pump unit controls to include: Control of water pump operation (internal and external as appropriate) Control of water temperature for the distribution system Control of outdoor fan operation for air to water units Defrost control of external airside heat exchanger for air to water systems External controls should include: Room thermostat to regulate the space temperature and interlocked with the HP unit operation
Gas engine driven heat pumps are currently available as variable refrigerant flow warm air systems	Multi-split Variable refrigerant flow	F	Controls package A above PLUS Heat pump unit controls to include: Control of room air temperature (if not provided externally) Control of outdoor fan operation Defrost control of external airside heat exchanger Control for secondary heating (if fitted) External controls should include: Room thermostat (if not provided internal to the HP) to regulate the space temperature and interlocked with the heat pump unit operation

If further measures are taken beyond these minimum provisions for controls, in order to exceed the minimum CoP for the proposed system, then the credits indicated in Table 12 can be added. This modified CoP (i.e. effective CoP) is entered in the accredited NCM tool when calculating the energy performance rating.

3.5 Heating Efficiency Credits for heat pump systems

Heating Efficiency Credits are available for measures over and above the minimum requirements which can be added to the CoP. The efficiency measures outlined in Table 10 are not required, but where they are adopted the relevant efficiency credit (percentage points) can be added to the minimum CoP (or to the manufacturer's rating, where this exceeds the minimum CoP) in order to calculate the Effective CoP.

In line with Equation 1 (Section 1.2): Effective CoP =
Coefficient of performance (%) + Total Heating Efficiency Credits

Table 12 Heating efficiency credits for measures applicable to heat pump systems in new and existing buildings

Measure	Heating efficiency credit		Comments/definition
	Ratio	(% points)	
<20% oversizing	0.02	2	The amount by which the *maximum heat pump output* exceeds heat output of the system at design conditions, expressed as a percentage of the system heat output
Optimised stop	0.02	2	A control system which stops plant operation at the earliest possible time such that internal conditions will not deteriorate beyond preset limits by the end of the occupancy period
Full zone control	0.02	2	Allowing each zone to operate independently in terms of start/stop time. Only applicable where operational conditions change in different zones
M & T system	0.02	2	Means of identifying changes in operation or onset of faults

Example 2: Using Heating Efficiency Credits to exceed the minimum CoP for a heat pump installation

The following example illustrates how Heating Efficiency Credits can be added to the efficiency of a heat pump system to exceed the minimum provisions.

The proposed building will have an air-to-water, electrically driven heat pump to be used with an underfloor heating system. When tested to EN 14511 the CoP was measured as 2.0 (200%) which meets the minimum provisions for this type of system.

The minimum controls package will be installed, that is:

- controls package A (zone control, demand control and time control) PLUS

- controls package B:

    – control of water pump operation and water temperature for the distribution system

    – control of outdoor fan operation for air to water units

    – defrost control of external airside heat exchanger for air to water systems

    – a room thermostat to regulate the space temperature and interlocked with the HP unit operation

In addition to the minimum controls package, optimised stop control and full zone control will be installed.

Table 13 shows how credits would be awarded to this example.

Table 13 Example to illustrate the allocation of Heating Efficiency Credits to a new heat pump system

Measure	Heat Plant Efficiency Credit (expressed as a ratio)
CoP single duct air-to-water heat pump	2.0 in this example (manufacturer's rating)
Measures specified in controls package A	0 (as minimum requirement)
Measures specified in controls package B	0 (as minimum requirement)
Optimised stop	0.02
Full zone control	0.02
Total credits	**0.04**

In line with Equation 1 (Section 1.2): Effective CoP = (CoP) + (Total Heating Efficiency Credits) = 2.0 + 0.04 = 2.04

The Effective CoP would therefore be 2.04, exceeding the minimum CoP. The value that would be entered in the accredited NCM tool to calculate an energy performance rating is 2.04.

Recommended good practice for heat pumps

Table 14 outlines further recommendations for heat pumps. It should be noted that these are not required for compliance with the Approved Documents ADL2A or ADL2B but are recommended as good practice.

Table 14 Recommended good practice for heat pumps

Heat source/sink	Technology	Comments
Air to air	Single package	Units may be ducted on one or other of the supply and return air sides or ducted on both sides. Ducting needs to be designed to take into account the maximum specific fan power allowable (see Section 10 of this guide) and to maintain the minimum allowable Coefficient of Performance
	Split system Multi-split system Variable refrigerant flow system Gas engine driven	A split system will comprise a single outdoor unit and a single indoor unit as a package. Multi-split and VRF systems will comprise a single outdoor unit and two or more indoor units as a package. Several packages may be used to satisfy the requirements of the building In order for efficiencies to be maintained all connecting pipework must be installed in accordance with manufacturer's recommendations (diameter, length, insulation and riser height). Any ducting needs to be designed to take into account the maximum specific fan power allowable and to maintain the minimum allowable Coefficient of Performance
Water or ground to air	Single package Energy transfer systems (matching heating/cooling demand in buildings)	Energy transfer systems generally consist of multiple water source heat pumps connected in parallel to a common closed water loop. They are installed to offset the simultaneous heating and cooling demand in a building due to the different loads present on the aspects of the building. Water circulation pumps for the closed loop need to be taken into consideration along with the fan power required for the cooling tower or dry cooler or energy for water pumps for the ground loop if this method is utilised for heat injection and rejection. Any ducting needs to be designed to take into account the maximum specific fan power allowable and to maintain the minimum allowable Coefficient of Performance
Air to water Water to ground or water	Single package Split package	Water circulation pumps for the delivery of heated water to the building need to be taken into consideration in the calculation. Additionally the energy of water pumps used for the heat source (water or ground) needs to be considered in the calculation. Any ducting needs to be designed to take into account the maximum specific fan power allowable and to maintain the minimum allowable Coefficient of Performance

Section 4 Gas and oil-fired warm air heaters

4.1 Introduction

This section outlines the minimum provisions needed to comply with Part L when space heating in new build and in existing buildings is provided by warm air heaters. It addresses the relevant types of warm air heaters and measures, such as controls, for which the associated energy efficiency benefits may be added to the Heat Generator Seasonal Efficiency.

Note that it is advisable to use the National Calculation Methodology (NCM) to determine the carbon performance of the proposed new building as some of the benefits of using warm air heaters are included in the calculation procedure.

4.2 Scope of the guidance

The guidance given in this section covers the types of warm air heater systems described in Table 15. The provisions of this section also cover indirect gas or oil-fired heat exchangers (as used in large ducted systems for office blocks, shopping and leisure complexes, etc.) to provide heating and fresh or conditioned air. Warm air central heating systems are not within the scope of this section.

Table 15 Warm air heaters and associated test methodologies

Type of warm air heater		Product standard
Type 1	Gas-fired forced convection without a fan to assist transportation of combustion air and/or combustion products	BS EN 621:1998[11]
Type 2	Gas-fired forced convection incorporating a fan to assist transportation of combustion air and/or combustion products	BS EN 1020:1998[12]
Type 3	Direct gas-fired forced convection	BS EN 525:1998[13]
Type 4	Oil-fired forced convection	BS EN 13842:2004[14]

4.3 Definitions

Heat Generator Seasonal Efficiency

As air heaters operate under the same conditions at all times their Heat Generator Seasonal Efficiency is equivalent to their measured steady state thermal efficiency (gross calorific value). Gross thermal efficiency will be obtained from the heater manufacturer's data. If the net efficiency is given this must be converted to a gross efficiency, using the conversion factors in Appendix 1 of this guide.

For indirect-fired heaters data values for net heat input and output are measured using the efficiency test methods described in EN 1020, EN 621 or EN 13842 as appropriate.

For direct-fired heaters the efficiency should be calculated using the method described in EN 525.

The calculation of the gross thermal efficiency should:

- Include the heater.

- Include associated products of combustion exhaust chimney within the building envelope.

- Exclude fans.

---

[11] BS EN 621:1998 Non domestic gas fired forced convection air heaters for space heating not exceeding a net heat input of 300kW, without a fan to assist transportation of combustion air. ISBN 0 580 295834.

[12] BS EN 1020:1998 Non domestic gas-fired convection air heaters for space heating not exceeding a net heat input of 300kW, incorporating a fan to assist transportation of combustion air and/or combustion products (AMD 13525).

[13] BS EN 525:1998 Non domestic direct gas-fired forced convection air heaters for space heating not exceeding a net input of 300kW.

[14] BS EN 13842:2004 Oil-fired convection air heaters – stationary and transportable for space heating.

4.4 Minimum provisions for warm air heaters in new and existing buildings

In order to comply with ADL2A and ADL2B, for warm air systems in new and existing buildings, the following minimum provisions should be met:

a.   The warm air system should achieve a minimum thermal efficiency (gross calorific value) (Heat Generator Efficiency) no worse than the applicable value in Table 16;

AND

b.   A minimum controls package should be adopted entailing time control AND space temperature control AND, for buildings with a floor area greater than 150m^2, zone control.

Table 16 Minimum thermal efficiencies for warm air heaters

Warm air heater type (as defined in Table 15)	Minimum thermal efficiency (gross calorific value)
Types 1, 2 and 4	80%
Type 3*	90%

*Note. For Type 3 air heaters 100% of the net heat input is delivered to the space. Specific ventilation requirements as defined in EN 525 must be met.

4.5 Heating Efficiency Credits for warm air heaters in new and existing buildings

Heating Efficiency Credits are available for measures listed in Table 17; however, these measures are optional. If these measures are adopted, the associated efficiency benefits can be added to the Heat Generating Seasonal Efficiency and inputted into the accredited NCM tool in order to improve the energy performance rating for the proposed building.

Therefore, when demonstrating compliance for new buildings the relevant efficiency value to input into the accredited NCM model is the applicable thermal efficiency value in Table 16 (or the manufacturer's rating for the appliance being specified, where it exceeds the relevant value in Table 16) plus any Heating Efficiency Credits.

Note that Heating Efficiency Credits are not available for the minimum controls package.

Table 17 Heating Efficiency Credits for measures applicable to warm air heaters

Measure	Heating Efficiency Credits (% points)	Comments/definition
Optimised shut down	1	A control system which stops plant operation at the earliest possible time such that internal conditions will not deteriorate beyond preset limits by the end of the occupancy period
Hi/lo burners	2	Two stage burners which enable two distinct firing rates
Modulating burners	3	Burner controls allow continuous adjustment between firing rates

Destratification fans and air-induction schemes

It is recognised that destratification fans and air-induction schemes may improve the efficiency of a warm air system and significantly reduce the carbon emissions associated with the heating system. The benefits associated with these measures are calculated in the accredited NCM tool. Note that warm air systems with air-induction schemes or destratification fans should not be confused with central heating with air distribution. (Warm air central heating systems are not within the scope of the Non-domestic Heating, Cooling and Ventilation Compliance Guide.)

Example 3: Using Heating Efficiency Credits to exceed the minimum Heat Generator Seasonal Efficiency for a warm air heater

The following example illustrates how Heating Efficiency Credits can be used to exceed the minimum Heat Generator Seasonal Efficiency for a warm air heater system.

The proposed building will have a gas-fired forced convection warm air heater without a fan to assist transportation of combustion air and/or combustion products. When tested to BS EN 621:1998 the efficiency is calculated as 80% which meets the minimum Heat Generator Efficiency requirement for this type of system.

The minimum controls package will be installed, i.e. zone, space temperature and time controls. In addition to the minimum controls requirement, optimised start/stop and modulating burners will be provided.

Table 18 shows how credits would be awarded in this example.

Table 18 Example to illustrate the allocation of Heating Efficiency Credits to a warm air heater system

Measure	Heating efficiency credits (% points)
Thermal efficiency of warm air heater	80%
Zone, space and temperature controls	0 (as minimum requirement)
Modulating burners	3
Optimised shut down	1
Total credits	**4**

From Equation 1 (Section 1.2): Effective Heat Generating Seasonal Efficiency = Gross Thermal Efficiency + Total Heating Efficiency Credits

$$= 80\% + 4\% = 84\%$$

Destratification fans will be also be installed providing seven volume changes per hour. But note that the efficiency benefits of the destratification measures are calculated in the accredited NCM tool.

The Effective Heat Generating Seasonal Efficiency would therefore be 84%, exceeding the minimum requirement by four percentage points. The value that would be entered in the accredited NCM tool to calculate an energy performance rating is 84%, expressed as a ratio (i.e. 0.84).

Section 5 Gas and oil-fired radiant technology

5.1 Introduction

This section outlines the minimum provisions needed to comply with Part L when space heating in new build and in existing buildings is provided by radiant heaters. It addresses the relevant radiant heater types and measures, such as controls, for which the associated energy efficiency benefits may be added to the Heat Generator Seasonal Efficiency.

Note that it is advisable to use the NCM to determine the carbon performance of the proposed new building as some of the benefits of using radiant heaters are included in the calculation procedure.

5.2 Scope of the guidance

The guidance given in this section covers the types of radiant heater systems outlined in Table 19 below:

Table 19 Types of radiant heater and associated product standards

Radiant heater type	Product standard
Luminous radiant heater	BS EN 419:2000[15]
Non-luminous radiant heater	BS EN 416-1:1999[16]
Multi-burner radiant heaters	BS EN 777 series[17]
Oil-fired radiant heaters	N/A

5.3 Definitions

Radiant Heater Seasonal Efficiency

For radiant heaters the Heat Generator Seasonal Efficiency is equivalent to its thermal efficiency (gross calorific value).

For flued appliances the thermal efficiency of the radiant heater will be stated by the manufacturer of the radiant heater having been measured according to the test standards EN 1020[18] or EN 13842[19] as applicable. The procedures in EN 1020 and EN 13842 yield a net efficiency – this must be converted to a gross efficiency, using the conversion factors in Appendix 1 of this guide.

The calculation of the thermal efficiency (gross calorific value) should:

- Include the radiant heater.

- Include associated flue pipe/tailpipe within the building envelope.

- Exclude fans.

For unflued heaters the minimum thermal efficiency levels given in Table 20 should be used.

---

[15] BS EN 419-1:2000 Non-domestic gas-fired overhead luminous radiant heaters. Safety.
[16] BS EN 416-1:1999 Single burner gas-fired overhead radiant-tube heaters. Safety.
[17] BS EN 777-1:1999 Multi-burner gas-fired overhead radiant tube heater systems for non-domestic use. System D, safety.
BS EN 777-2:1999 Multi-burner gas-fired overhead radiant tube heater systems for non-domestic use. System E, safety.
BS EN 777-3:2000 Multi-burner gas-fired overhead radiant tube heater systems for non-domestic use. System F, safety.
BS EN 777-4:1999 Multi-burner gas-fired overhead radiant tube heater systems for non-domestic use. System H, safety.
[18] BS EN 1020 Non domestic gas-fired convection air heaters for space heating not exceeding a net heat input of 300kW, incorporating a fan to assist transportation of combustion air and/or combustion products (AMD 13525).
BS EN 13842:2004 Oil-fired convection air heaters – stationary and transportable for space heating.
[19] BS EN 13842:2004 Oil-fired convection air heaters – stationary and transportable for space heating.

5.4 Minimum provisions for radiant heaters

In order to comply with ADL2A and ADL2B, for radiant heaters in new and existing buildings, the following minimum provisions should be met:

a.   The radiant heater system should achieve a minimum Heat Generator Seasonal Efficiency, that is a thermal efficiency (gross calorific value), of no less than the relevant value in Table 20;

AND

b.   A minimum controls package should be adopted entailing time control and space temperature control with black bulb sensors.

Table 20 Minimum thermal efficiency levels (Heat Generator Seasonal Efficiency) for radiant heater technology

Appliance type	Minimum thermal efficiency (gross calorific value) %
Luminous radiant heater (unflued)	85.5
Non-luminous radiant heater (unflued)	85.5
Non-luminous radiant heater (flued)	73.8
Multi-burner radiant heaters	80

5.5 Heating Efficiency Credits for radiant heaters in new and existing buildings

Heating Efficiency Credits are available for measures listed in Table 21; however, these measures are optional. If these measures are adopted, the associated efficiency benefits can be added to the Heat Generating Seasonal Efficiency and input into the accredited NCM tool in order to improve the energy performance rating for the proposed building.

Therefore, when demonstrating compliance for new buildings the relevant efficiency value to input into the accredited NCM model is the applicable thermal efficiency value in Table 20 (or the manufacturer's rating for the appliance being specified, where it exceeds the relevant value in Table 20) plus any Heating Efficiency Credits.

Note that Heating Efficiency Credits are not available for the minimum controls package.

It is recognised that the efficiency of a heating system using radiant heaters improves with increasing room height. These efficiency benefits arise from a reduction in the ventilation and fabric losses. The efficiency benefits are assigned in the accredited NCM tool.

Table 21 Heating Efficiency Credits for measures applicable to radiant heaters

Measure		Heating Efficiency Credits % points	Comments/definition
Controls (additional to the minimum package)	Optimised shut down	1	A control system which stops plant operation at the earliest possible time such that internal conditions will not deteriorate beyond preset limits by the end of the occupancy period
	Zone control	1	Allowing each zone to operate independently in terms of start/stop time. Only applicable where operational conditions change in different zones

Example 4: Using Heating Efficiency Credits to exceed the minimum Heat Generator Seasonal Efficiency for a radiant heater system

The proposed building will have a flued non-luminous radiant heater system with a gross thermal efficiency of 73.8%. A black bulb sensor and an optimiser will be fitted.

The Heating Efficiency Credits associated with these measures (in Table 21) may be added to the appliance thermal efficiency in order to achieve an Effective Heat Generating Seasonal Efficiency which exceeds the minimum provisions. Table 22 shows how credits would be awarded for this example.

Table 22 Example to illustrate the allocation of Heating Efficiency Credits to a radiant heater system

Measure	Heating Efficiency Credits (% points)
Gross thermal efficiency of radiant heater (converted from net value given by EN 1020)	73.8%
Black bulb sensor (minimum requirement)	0
Optimised shut down	1
Zone control	1
Total credits	**2**

In this example the Heat Generating Seasonal Efficiency is calculated as follows:

From Equation 1 (Section 1.2): Effective Heat Generating Seasonal Efficiency = Gross Thermal Efficiency (73.8%) + Total Heating Efficiency Credits (2%) = 75.8%

In this example, the radiant heater system exceeds the minimum provisions for a thermal efficiency of 73.8%. The value that would be entered in the accredited NCM tool to calculate an energy performance rating is 75.8% – this value should be expressed as ratio (i.e. 0.758).

Section 6 Combined Heat and Power (CHP) and community heating

6.1 Introduction

This section outlines the minimum provisions needed to comply with Part L when space heating in new build and in existing buildings is provided by Combined Heat and Power (CHP). It addresses the relevant CHP technologies and measures, such as controls, that may be used to improve the efficiency of the heat generator.

CHP units are normally used in conjunction with boilers. The majority of the annual heat demand is usually supplied from the CHP plant and the boilers are used to meet peak demands and for periods when the CHP unit is not operating either for economic considerations, for example at night, or during maintenance downtime. CHP units may on a relatively small scale supply single buildings or, on a larger scale, supply a number of buildings through a Community Heating system. The most common fuel is natural gas which can be used in spark-ignition gas engines, micro-turbines, or gas turbines in open cycle or combined cycle.

This section gives the minimum provisions for CHP units which may or may not supply community heating. Guidance on community heating systems (including those with heat generators other than CHP) is available in the Domestic Heating Compliance Guide published by the ODPM in support of Part L of the Building Regulations.

6.2 Scope of the guidance

The guidance in this section covers all types of CHP systems used in commercial applications.

6.3 Definitions

Combined Heat and Power Quality Assurance (CHPQA)

CHPQA[20] is a scheme under which registration and certification of CHP schemes is carried out in accordance with the criterion for Good Quality CHP.

CHPQA Quality Index (CHP(QI))

This is an indicator of the energy efficiency and environmental performance of a CHP scheme, relative to the generation of the same amounts of heat and power by separate, alternative means.

6.4 Minimum provisions for CHP in new and existing buildings

In order to comply with ADL2A and ADL2B, for CHP units in new and existing buildings, the following minimum provisions should be met:

    a.   The CHP plant shall achieve a minimum CHPQA Quality Index of 105;

AND

    b.   As a minimum, the control system shall ensure that the CHP unit operates as the lead heat generator;

AND

    c.   Metering shall be provided to measure the hours run, the electricity generated and the fuel supplied to the CHP unit;

AND

    d.   For peak and standby boilers, the minimum boiler efficiencies and minimum controls apply as in Section 2 of this guide.

---

[20]   Further information about the CHPQA programme is available on the website: www.chpqa.com

The CHP should be sized to supply no less than 45% of the annual total heating demand (i.e. space heating, domestic hot water heating and process heating) unless there are overriding practical or economic constraints.

Total CO_2 emissions from CHP – data input for NCM tools (e.g. SBEM)

CHP may be used as the main or supplementary heat source in Community Heating or District Heating schemes. In calculating the total CO_2 emissions for a new building to show compliance, the following data shall be entered into the accredited NCM tool (e.g. SBEM):

1.   The proportion of the annual heat demand (H) supplied from the CHP plant (P). This is needed as the CHP unit is normally sized below the peak heat demand of the building and will also be out of service for maintenance purposes.

2.   The overall efficiency ratio of the CHP plant (E) as defined in Equation 5 and taking account of part load operation and all heat rejection predicted by an operating model.

*Overall efficiency E = annual useful heat supplied + annual electricity generated
(net of parasitic electricity use) divided by the annual energy of the fuel supplied
(in gross calorific value terms)*   **Equation 5**

3.   The heat to power ratio of the CHP plant (R) is calculated for the annual operation according to Equation 6:

*Heat to power ratio (R) = annual useful heat supplied divided by annual electricity
generated (net of parasitic electricity use)*   **Equation 6**

From these parameters, the SBEM model (or other accredited NCM model) will calculate the CO_2 emissions in the heat supplied from the CHP plant using an emissions factor for the electricity generated by the CHP of 568g/kWh applied to the annual total of electricity generation.

The annual CO_2 emissions for the heat supplied by a CHP plant (assuming gas-fired) is given by Equation 7:

*Annual CO_2 emissions for the heat supplied by a CHP plant =
$((H \times P)/E) + (H \times P)/(R \times E)) \times 194 - ((H \times P)/R) \times 568$*   **Equation 7**

(CO_2 emissions are in kg for the heat demand H in MWh)
where the terms H, P, E and R are defined above.

The CO_2 emissions for the balance of heat supplied by the boilers is then calculated by the SBEM model as for a boiler only system.

6.5 Additional guidance for community heating in new and existing buildings

The design of the community heating (CH) connection and the building's heating control system shall take account of the requirements of the CH Organisation with respect to maintaining low return temperatures at part load and limiting the maximum flow rate to be supplied by the CH system to the agreed level. A heat meter shall be installed to measure the heat energy supplied and to monitor the maximum heat demand, the maximum CH flow rate and the return temperatures onto the CH network.

Further guidance can be found in the following documents:

•   Carbon Trust GPG 234 – Community Heating and CHP

•   CIBSE AM12 – Small-scale CHP for buildings

At the time of writing, the guidance for micro-CHP is still under development and is expected to include:

•   A Good Practice Guide specifying the minimum standards for installation and control of micro-CHP

•   Publicly Available Specification – PAS 67 Laboratory test to determine heating and electrical performance of heat-led micro-cogeneration packages primarily intended for heating dwellings.

Section 7 Electric space heating

7.1 Introduction

This section outlines the minimum provisions needed to comply with Part L when space heating in new build and in existing buildings is provided by electric heaters. It addresses the relevant electric heater types and the minimum provision of controls.

7.2 Scope of the guidance

The guidance given in this section covers the following types of electric heating systems which may be used to provide primary or secondary space heating:

- Electric boilers

- Electric warm air systems (not including electric warm air central heating systems)

- Electric panel heaters

- Electric storage systems including integrated storage/direct systems

- Electric fan heaters and fan convector heaters

- Electric radiant heaters including quartz and ceramic types

The guidance does not cover electric heat pumps or portable electric heating devices.

7.3 Definitions

The electric heating devices in this section are assumed to be 100% thermally efficient in conversion of electricity to heat within the building and therefore a Minimum Heat Generating Seasonal Efficiency is not defined.

7.4 Minimum provisions for electric space heating in new and existing buildings

In order to comply with ADL2A and ADL2B, for electric space heating systems in new and existing buildings, the following minimum provisions should be met:

a.   Electric boilers should meet the minimum provisions for controls given in Table 23.

b.   Electric space heating systems, other than boilers, should meet the minimum provisions for controls given in Table 24.

Table 23 Minimum provisions for control of electric boiler systems

	Minimum provision	Comments
Boiler temperature control	The boiler should be fitted with a flow temperature control and be capable of modulating the power input to the primary water depending on space heating conditions.	See Note 1
Zoning	Buildings with a total usable floor area up to 150m^2 should be divided into at least two zones with independent temperature control. For buildings with a total usable floor area greater than 150m^2, at least two space heating zones must be provided, each having separate timing and temperature controls, by either: (i) multiple heating zone programmers; or (ii) a single multi-channel programmer.	If the building floor area is less than 150m^2 sub-zoning of temperature control is not appropriate. See Note 1
Temperature control of space heating	Separate temperature control of zones within the building, using either: (i) room thermostats or programmable room thermostats in all zones; or (ii) a room thermostat or programmable room thermostat in the main zone and individual radiator controls such as Thermostatic Radiator Valves (TRVs) on all radiators in the other zones; or (iii) a combination of (i) and (ii) above.	See Note 1
Time control of space and water heating	Time control of space and water heating should be provided by: (i) a full programmer with separate timing to each circuit; (ii) two or more separate timers providing timing control to each circuit; or (iii) programmable room thermostat(s) to the heating circuit(s), with separate timing of each circuit.	See Note 1

Note 1: An acceptable alternative to this is any boiler management control system that meets the specified zoning, timing and temperature requirements.

Table 24 Minimum provisions for control of primary and secondary electric heating systems (other than electric boilers)

Electric heating system	Requirement	Reasonable provision	Comments
Electric warm air systems	Time and temperature control, either integral to the heater or external	(i) A time switch/programmer and room stat OR (ii) a programmable room thermostat	
	Zone control – for buildings with a total usable floor area greater than 150m² more than one space heating circuit should be provided, each having separate timing and temperature controls	(i) Multiple heating zone programmers OR (ii) a single multi-channel programmer	
Electric radiant heaters	Zone or occupancy control	Connection to a passive infrared detector	Electric radiant heaters can provide zone heating or be used for a full heating scheme. Common electric radiant heaters include the quartz or ceramic type
Panel/skirting heaters	Local time and temperature control	(i) Time control provided by a programmable time switch integrated into the appliance OR a separate time switch (ii) Individual temperature control provided by integral thermostats OR by separate room thermostats	Panel heater systems provide instantaneous heat
Storage heaters	Charge control	Automatic control of input charge (ability to detect the internal temperature and adjust the charging of the heater accordingly)	
	Temperature control	Manual controls for adjusting the rate of heat release from the appliance such as adjustable damper or some other thermostatically controlled means	
Fan/fan convector heaters	Local fan control	A switch integrated into the appliance OR a separate remote switch	
	Individual temperature control	Integral switches or separate remote switching	

Section 8 Domestic hot water

8.1 Introduction

This section outlines the minimum provisions needed to comply with Part L when domestic hot water systems are provided in new build and in existing buildings. It addresses the relevant hot water system types and measures, such as controls, for which the associated energy efficiency benefits may be added to the Heat Generator Seasonal Efficiency.

As well as Building Regulations, other regulations apply to the provision of domestic hot water systems and energy-saving measures should not compromise the safety of people or the ability of the system to achieve approved regimes for the control of legionella.

For guidance on solar hot water systems, refer to the Domestic Heating Compliance Guide which is published by NBS in support of Building Regulations Part L and the NBS publication Low or Zero Carbon Energy Sources – Strategic Guide.

8.2 Scope of the guidance

The guidance in this section covers conventional gas, electric and oil-fired systems.

The minimum provisions of this section apply only to dedicated water heaters. Therefore, the efficiency performance of central heating boilers which provide space heating and domestic hot water should be as in Section 2 of this guide.

Solar hot water systems are not within the scope of this guide; however, in the UK they are normally operated with a back-up source of heat such as gas or electricity, so the guidance in this section will apply to the back-up system.

The types of domestic hot water systems covered in this section are shown in Table 25.

Table 25 Types of hot water systems covered by the Non-domestic Heating, Cooling and Ventilation Compliance Guide

DHW system type	Definition
Indirect natural gas, LPG and oil-fired systems	A system in which the water is supplied to the draw-off points from a device in which water is heated by means of an element through which the heating medium is circulated in such a manner that it does not mix with the hot water supply. In practice these are likely to be boilers dedicated to the supply of DHW and therefore would meet the minimum requirements of the Boiler Efficiency Directive
Direct-fired storage water heater system (natural gas, LPG and oil-fired)	A system in which the water is supplied to the draw-off points from a hot water vessel in which water is heated by combustion gases from a primary energy source
Electric water heaters	
Point of use electrically heated water heater systems	A system in which the water is supplied to the draw-off points from a device in which water is heated by an electric element or elements immersed in the stored water. The water heater is situated in close proximity to the draw-off points (point of use) and should have a storage capacity no greater than 100 litres
Instantaneous electrically heated water heater systems	A system in which the water is supplied to the draw-off points from a device in which the water is heated by an electric element or elements that heat the cold water as it flows through the water heater. The water heater is situated in close proximity to the draw-off points. The unit has no storage volume as water is instantaneously heated as it flows through the device
Local electrically heated water heater systems	A system in which the water is supplied to the draw-off points from a device in which water is heated by an electric element or elements immersed in the stored water. The water heater is situated in the locality of the draw-off points and should have a storage capacity of between 100 and 300 litres. Bulk heating of the water heater should be arranged to occur using off peak electricity supplies
Centralised electrically heated water heater systems	A system in which the water is supplied to the draw-off points from a device in which water is heated by an electric element or elements immersed in the stored water. The water heater is situated centrally with a distribution system to supply water to the draw-off points and should have a capacity greater than 300 litres. Bulk heating of the water heater should be arranged to occur using off peak electricity supplies

8.3 Definitions

The heat generator seasonal efficiency is defined for each system type in Table 26.

The **Effective Heat Generating Seasonal Efficiency** is the heat generator seasonal efficiency plus heating efficiency credits gained by adopting measures in Table 29.

Table 26 Definition of Heat Generator Seasonal Efficiency for DHW systems

DHW system type	Heat Generator Seasonal Efficiency	Components to include in calculation of Heat Generator Seasonal Efficiency*
Direct fired systems (gas- and oil-fired)	The thermal efficiency of the heater (gross calorific value) when tested using the procedures in BS EN 89:2000[21] ***Gross thermal efficiency = Output of the heater divided by the gross input*** **Equation 8** where the heater output is defined as follows: Output of the heater = Recovery rate of heater in litres/second x specific heat capacity of water x temperature rise of the water **Equation 9**	For direct systems include the water heater and insulation of the allied storage vessel only Exclude the following components: • secondary pipework • fans and pumps • diverter valves, solenoids, actuators • supplementary storage vessels
Indirect-fired systems (gas- and oil-fired)	The Heat Generator Seasonal Efficiency of the heat generator (boiler) allied to an indirect storage cylinder should be calculated using Equation 2, 3.1, or 3.2 and 3.3 (as appropriate) as given in Section 2 of this guide. If Seasonal Boiler Efficiency values are obtained as net values the conversion factors in Appendix 1 should be used to convert to a gross value	For indirect cylinder systems include the heat generator only
Electric systems	Point of use electrically heated water heater systems	These are assumed 100% thermally efficient in terms of conversion to heat within the building
	Local electrically heated water heater systems	These are assumed 100% thermally efficient in terms of conversion to heat within the building
	Centralised electrically heated water heater systems	These are assumed 100% thermally efficient in terms of conversion to heat within the building

*Note: For hot water systems in new buildings, standing losses are calculated in the accredited NCM tool.

8.4 Minimum provisions for domestic hot water systems in new and existing buildings

In order to comply with ADL2A and ADL2B, for domestic hot water systems in new and existing buildings, the following minimum provisions should be met:

a. Direct fired domestic hot water systems should have a minimum thermal efficiency (gross calorific value) no worse than 73% if fired by natural gas; or 74% if fired by LPG; or 75% if fired by oil.

Indirect cylinder systems (boilers dedicated to hot water supply) should have a minimum Heat Generator Seasonal Efficiency (gross calorific value) of no less than 80% for natural gas-fired systems; or no less than 81% for LPG systems; or no less than 82% for oil-fired systems.

Note all electrically-heated water heaters have a heating efficiency of 100% at the point of energy conversion.

AND

b. A minimum controls package should be adopted as in Table 27 for gas, LPG and oil-fired systems and electric systems.

---

[21] BS EN 89:2000 Gas fired water heaters for the production of domestic hot water.

Table 27 Minimum controls package for domestic hot water systems

Type of DHW system	Minimum controls package
Gas- and oil-fired direct fired hot water systems	• Automatic thermostat control to shut off the burner/primary heat supply when the desired temperature of the hot water has been reached • Time control
Gas- and oil-fired indirect systems	• Automatic thermostat control to shut off the burner/primary heat supply when the desired temperature of the hot water has been reached • High limit thermostat to shut off primary flow if system temperature too high • Time control

Electric domestic hot water systems

	Point of use electrically heated water heater systems	Local electrically heated water heater systems	Centralised electrically heated water heater systems	Instantaneous electrically heated water heater systems
Automatic thermostat control to interrupt the electrical supply when the desired storage temperature has been reached	Yes	Yes	Yes	x
High limit thermostat (thermal cut-out) to interrupt the energy supply if the system temperature gets too high	Yes	Yes	Yes	x
Manual reset in the event of an over-temperature trip	Yes	Yes	Yes	x
A 7-day time-clock (or BMS interface) should be provided to ensure bulk heating of water using off peak electricity. The facility to boost the temperature using on peak electricity (ideally by means of an immersion heater fitted to heat the top 30% of the cylinder) should be provided	x	Yes	Yes	x
High limit thermostat (thermal cut-out) to interrupt the energy supply if the outlet temperature gets too high. (Note: outlet temperature is controlled by rate of flow through the unit which on basic units would be by the outlet tap or fitting.)	x	x	x	Yes
Flow sensor that only allows electrical input should sufficient flow through the unit be achieved	x	x	x	Yes

For electric water heaters additional guidance is provided in Table 28 – this is not however required in order to meet the minimum provisions for compliance with Part L.

Table 28 Additional guidance for construction of electric water heaters

Point of use electrically heated water heater systems	These should be constructed to comply with BS EN 60335-2-21:1999[22] and the heat loss should not exceed 1.28 x (0.2 + 0.051$V^{2/3}$) kWh where V is the cylinder's nominal capacity in litres
Instantaneous electrically heated water heater systems	These should be constructed to comply with BS EN 60335-2-35:2002[23]
Local electrically heated water heater systems	Vented systems These should be constructed to comply with BS EN 60335-2-21 OR BS 1566-1:2002[24] OR BS 3198:1981[25] for vented systems Unvented systems These should be constructed to comply with BS 7206 and/or be certified by the BBA, WRC-NSF or other accredited body as complying with Building Regulation G3 for unvented systems The heat loss should not exceed 1.28 x (0.051V)$^{2/3}$ kWh where V is the nominal capacity of the cylinder in litres
Centralised electrically heated water heater systems	The vessel should be constructed to comply with BS 853[26] Bulk heating of the water should utilise off peak electricity where possible When using off peak electricity a 'Boost Heater' should be fitted to allow 'on peak' heating. The 'Boost Heater' should heat the top 30% of the cylinder and be rated to approximately 30% of the main off peak heater battery; however the kW load will depend on the recovery time required The heater battery should be of either removable core or rod element construction. Removable core construction allows elements to be changed without removing the heater from the vessel or draining the system. For removable core construction, the maximum element watts density must not exceed 3W/cm^2 for copper tubes or 2.5W/cm^2 for stainless steel tubes. For rod element construction, elements should be of Nickel Alloy 825 sheath, be U-bent and have a maximum watts density of 10W/cm^2 Temperature control should be by means of 'on/off' control of the heater battery utilising stage ramping for kW loadings above 30kW. Thermostatic control is an ideal solution The control sensor should be mounted in the cylinder at an angle of approximately 45° to the heater and at a level just above the heating bundle. The over temperature sensor (high limit) should be mounted in the top 30% of the cylinder directly above the heater bundle. A manual reset should be required in the event of an over-temperature trip For loadings greater than 6kW temperature sensors should not be fitted to the heater bundle. This is to prevent thermostat and contactor cycling which will lead to premature failure of the equipment and poor temperature control

8.5 Heating Efficiency Credits for domestic hot water systems

Heating Efficiency Credits are available for measures listed in Table 29; however, these measures are optional. If these measures are adopted, the associated efficiency benefits can be added to the Heat Generating Seasonal Efficiency and entered into the accredited NCM tool in order to improve the energy performance rating for the proposed building.

[22]   BS EN 60335-2-21:1999 Specification for safety of household and similar electrical appliances. Particular requirements for storage water heaters.
[23]   BS EN 60335-2-35:2002 Specification for safety of household and similar electrical appliances. Particular requirements for instantaneous water heaters.
[24]   BS 1566-1:2002 Copper indirect cylinders for domestic purposes. Open vented copper cylinders. Requirements and test methods.
[25]   BS 3198:1981 Specification for copper hot water storage combination units for domestic purposes.
[26]   BS 853-1: Calorifiers and storage vessels for central heating and hot water supplies.

When demonstrating compliance for new buildings the relevant efficiency value to input into the accredited NCM model is the Effective Heat Generating Seasonal Efficiency as in Equation 1 (repeated):

Effective Heat Generating Seasonal Efficiency =
Heat Generator Seasonal Efficiency + Total Heating Efficiency Credits   **Equation 1**

where the Heat Generator Seasonal Efficiency is:

- The applicable thermal efficiency value for direct fired systems (or the manufacturer's rating for the appliance being specified, where it exceeds the minimum provisions); OR

- The Seasonal Boiler Efficiency for indirect gas- or oil-fired systems (or the manufacturer's rating for the appliance being specified, where it exceeds the minimum provisions).

Note that Heating Efficiency Credits are not available for the minimum controls package.

Table 29 Heating Efficiency Credits for measures applicable to domestic hot water systems

System type	Measure	Heating efficiency credits %
All system types	Decentralisation	2 (not applicable to systems in new buildings)
Direct fired	Integral combustion circuit shut-off device	1
	Fully automatic ignition controls	0.5
All system types	Confirming correct size of unit by using manufacturer's technical help lines and using manufacturer's sizing software	2

Example 5: Using Heating Efficiency Credits to exceed the minimum Heat Generator Seasonal Efficiency for a direct fired system

Step 1: calculating thermal efficiency of direct-fired DHW system

- Recovery rate of heater = 0.4694 litres/second

- Gross input rate of heater = 128kW

- Specific heat capacity of water = 4.187kJ/kg°C

- Temperature rise of water inside heater = 50°C

The heater output is calculated from Equation 9: *Output of the heater = Recovery rate of heater in litres/second x specific heat capacity of water x temperature rise of the water.*

$$0.4694 \div 4.187 \times 50 = 96.26\text{kW output}$$

The gross thermal efficiency is therefore calculated from Equation 8: *Gross thermal efficiency = Output of the heater divided by the gross input.*

$$96.26 \div 128 = 0.76$$

Step 2: adding Heating Efficiency Credits for additional measures

The heater has been sized to closely match the system demand by using the manufacturer's sizing guide and it will be fitted with fully automatic controls.

Table 30 shows how credits would be assigned in this example.

Table 30 Example to illustrate allocation of Heating Efficiency Credits for a DHW system	
Measure	**Heating Efficiency Credit – % points**
Sized according to manufacturer's guidance	2
Fully automatic ignition controls	0.5
Total credits	**2.5**

Heat Generating Seasonal Efficiency = Gross Thermal Efficiency + Total Heating Efficiency Credits
Therefore 76 + 2.5 = 78.5

The Effective Heat Generating Seasonal Efficiency would therefore be 78.5%. For this example, the value that would be entered in the NCM tool is 78.5% expressed as a ratio (i.e. 0.785).

Section 9 Comfort Cooling

9.1 Introduction

This section outlines the minimum provisions needed to comply with Part L when comfort cooling is provided in new build and in existing buildings. It addresses the relevant types of cooling technologies and measures, such as controls, that may be used to improve the overall efficiency. The purpose is to demonstrate the plant is sufficiently efficient and provide guidance on the use of the NCM (SBEM). It is not intended to replace the normal design process.

9.2 Scope of the guidance

This document deals with the specification of the efficiency of the refrigeration plant that is used in the SBEM tool and defined as the seasonal Energy Efficiency Ratio. The SBEM tool allocates standard correction factors[27] to the performance of cooling plant to account for the use of the different systems of distributing cooling to the spaces. Evaporative cooling and desiccant cooling systems are not within the scope of this guidance.

9.3 Definitions

Cooling plant

The cooling plant is that part of a cooling system that produces the supply of cooling medium. It does not include means of distributing the cooling medium or the delivery of the cooling into the relevant zone. It may consist, for example, of a single chiller or a series of chillers.

Cooling system

The cooling system is the complete system that is installed to provide the comfort cooling to the space. It includes the cooling plant and the system by which the cooling medium effects cooling in the relevant zone and the associated controls. This will in some cases be a complete packaged air conditioner.

Energy Efficiency Ratio (EER)

For chillers, the EER is the ratio of the cooling energy delivered into the cooling system divided by the energy input to the cooling plant as determined by BS EN 14511[28].

In the case of packaged air conditioners, the EER is the ratio of the energy removed from air within the conditioned space divided by the effective energy input to the unit as determined by BS EN 14511 or other appropriate standard procedure. The test conditions for determining EER are those specified in BS EN 14511.

Part Load Energy Efficiency Ratio

The Part Load Energy Efficiency Ratio is the ratio of the cooling energy delivered into the cooling system divided by the energy input to the cooling plant. The conditions at which part load performance is determined for individual chillers are based on chilled water provision of 7°C out/ 12°C in, at all load conditions, and are defined as follows:

Percentage part load	25%	50%	75%	100%
Air cooled chillers ambient entering air (°C)	20	25	30	35
Water cooled chillers entering condenser water (°C)	18	22	26	30

---

[27] Details of these, and how they have been derived, are available in the Manual of the UK National Methodology for Calculating the Energy Performance of Non-Domestic Buildings, on the DCLG website.
[28] BS EN 14511 (2004) Air conditioners, liquid chilling packages and heat pumps with electrically driven compressors for space heating and cooling. Test conditions.

Flow rate is assumed to be constant on basis of 35°C leaving at 100% load, i.e. a 5°C spread. (Note: If minimum compressor capacity is above 25%, then it is assumed that control will be by cycling the compressor. In that case a 0.9 'cycling factor' will be applied to reduce the actual minimum load EER the manufacturer can achieve.)

Seasonal Energy Efficiency Ratio (SEER)

SEER is the ratio of the total amount of cooling energy provided, divided by the total energy input to the cooling plant (which may comprise more than one cooling unit), summed over the year.

Where an industry approved test procedure for obtaining performance measurements of cooling plant at partial load conditions exists, the SEER of the cooling plant may be estimated from the EER of the cooling plant measured at partial load conditions, adjusted for the cooling load profile of the proposed building. Equation 10 illustrates how to determine the seasonal efficiency of the cooling plant at four steps of load control for a single chiller well matched to the applied load:

$$SEER = a\ (EER_{25}) + b\ (EER_{50}) + c\ (EER_{75}) + d\ (EER_{100})$$
Equation 10

where:

EER_x is the EER measured at the defined partial load conditions of 100%, 75%, 50% and 25%, and

a, b, c and d are the load profile weighting factors relevant to the proposed application.

9.4 Minimum provisions for comfort cooling in new and existing buildings

In order to comply with ADL2A and ADL2B, for comfort cooling systems in new and existing buildings, the following minimum provisions should be met:

    a.   Each cooling unit of the cooling plant shall achieve a minimum full load Energy Efficiency Ratio (EER) no worse than those in Table 31;

    AND

    b.   The minimum controls package specified in Table 32 shall be adopted.

Table 31 Minimum Energy Efficiency Ratio (EER) for comfort cooling

Type		Minimum cooling plant full load EER
Packaged air conditioners	Single duct types	1.8
	Other types	2.2
Split and multi-split air conditioners including variable refrigerant flow systems		2.4
Vapour compression cycle chillers, water cooled		3.4
Vapour compression cycle chillers, air cooled		2.25
Water loop heat pump		3.2
Absorption cycle chillers		0.5
Gas engine driven variable refrigerant flow		1.0

Table 32 Minimum controls for comfort cooling in new and existing buildings

	Minimum controls
Cooling plant	• Multiple cooling modules should be provided with controls to provide the most efficient operating modes for the combined plant
Cooling system	• Each terminal unit capable of providing cooling must be capable of time and temperature control either by its own, or remote, controls
	• In any given zone simultaneous heating and cooling shall be prevented by a suitable interlock

9.5 Calculating the SEER for the NCM (SBEM)

The value of the SEER to be used in the SBEM tool can be calculated in a number of ways according to the availability of information and application. The following section describes how the SEER may be calculated for situations where suitable data exist to a greater or lesser extent. The situations are:

- Chillers with no part load performance data

- Unknown load profiles

- Office type buildings

- Other building types with known load profile data.

For chillers that have no part load data

For chillers that have no part load data then the full load EER is taken as the SEER.

When load profile is not known

For applications where the load profile under which the cooling plant operates is not known but there are some data on chiller part load EER then:

- For chillers where the full and half load (50%) EER are known then the average of the EERs is taken as the SEER: i.e. the 100% and 50% are equally weighted.

- For chillers with four points of part load EER equation 10 is used with each EER weighted equally: i.e. a, b, c and d equal 0.25 each.

- In the event that the chiller used does not have data for four steps of load then the weights are apportioned appropriately.

For office type of accommodation

For applications in general office type accommodation the weighting factors as in the table below can be taken as representative of the load profile:

a	b	c	d
0.20	0.36	0.32	0.12

Other buildings with known load profile

If the load profile is known in detail, from more detailed simulation or prediction, then the appropriate weights may be used together with the appropriate EERs at those loads and the SEER may be derived as above and used as input to SBEM.

Examples

1. For a single chiller with EER of 2.9 (known at full load only) then the input of SEER to SBEM is 2.9.

2. For a chiller with 100% and 50% EERs of 2.0 and 2.5 respectively in a building with unknown load profile the SEER would be 2.25.

3. For a chiller with unknown application load profile and part load EERs of

$$EER_{100} = 4.89$$
$$EER_{75} = 4.42$$
$$EER_{50} = 3.93$$
$$EER_{25} = 2.59$$
$$SEER = 0.25 \times 2.59 + 0.25 \times 3.93 + 0.25 \times 4.42 + 0.25 \times 4.89 = 3.96$$

4. If the above chiller was to be used in an office and the typical UK weighting factors used then the SEER would be:

$$SEER = 0.2 \times 2.59 + 0.36 \times 3.93 + 0.32 \times 4.42 + 0.12 \times 4.89 = 3.93$$

Multiple chiller systems

For systems with multiple chillers for use in office buildings, combined EER values may be calculated based on the sum of the energy consumptions of all the operating chillers. In this case care must be taken to include all of the factors that can influence the combined performance of the multiple chiller installation. These will include:

- degree of oversizing of the total installed capacity

- sizing of individual chillers

- EERs of individual chillers

- control mode for the multiple chiller, e.g. parallel or sequential

- load profile of the proposed cooling load.

When these are known it may be possible to calculate a SEER which matches more closely the proposed installation than the simplifications described earlier.

Systems with free cooling and/or heat recovery

Systems that have the ability to use free cooling and/or heat recovery can achieve greater SEERs than more conventional systems. In these cases the SEER must be derived for the specific application under consideration.

Absorption chillers and district cooling

Absorption chillers may be used in conjunction with on-site CHP or from a Community or District Heating system. The CO_2 emissions will be calculated as for the use of CHP for heating. The control system shall ensure as far as possible that heat from boilers is not used to supply the absorption chiller.

Where a District Cooling scheme exists, connection to the system may result in lower CO_2 emissions if the cooling is produced centrally from CHP/absorption chillers, heat pumps or high efficiency vapour compression chillers. The District Cooling company will provide information on the CO_2 content of the cooling energy supplied, and this figure can then be used in calculating the CO_2 emissions for the building to demonstrate compliance.

Section 10 Air distribution systems

This section outlines the minimum provisions needed to comply with Part L when air distribution systems are provided in new build and in existing buildings.

10.1 Scope of the guidance

The guidance in this section applies to the following types of air handling systems:

- Central mechanical ventilation – including heating, cooling and heat recovery

- Central mechanical ventilation with heating and cooling

- All central systems not covered by the two points above

- Local ventilation only units within the local area, such as window/wall/roof units, serving one room or area

- Local ventilation only units remote from the area, such as ceiling void or roof-mounted units serving one room or area. This also includes fan assisted terminal VAV units where the primary air and cooling is provided by central plant

- Other local units, e.g. fan coil units.

Gas- and oil-fired air heaters installed within the area to be heated are not within the scope of this section.

10.2 Definitions

Specific fan power of an air distribution system

The specific fan power of an air distribution system (SFP) is defined as the sum of the design total circuit-watts, including all losses through switchgear and controls such as inverters, of the fans in the system that supply air and exhaust it back to outdoors (i.e. the sum of the total circuit-watts for supply and extract fans), divided by the design air flow rate through that system.

For the purpose of this guide, the specific fan power of an air distribution system should be calculated according to the procedure set out in Annex D 'Assessing the Power Efficiency of Fans and Air Handling Units – Calculating and Checking the SFP$_V$' of Draft prEN 13779, April 2005, 'Ventilation for Non-Residential Buildings – Performance Requirements for Ventilation and Room-Conditioning Systems'. Note, however, the definition includes power losses through switchgear and controls, as in Equation 11:

$$SFP = \frac{P_{sf} + P_{ef}}{q}$$

Equation 11

where *SFP* is the specific fan power demand of the air distribution system (W/(litre/s))

P_{sf} is the total fan power of all supply air fans at the design air flow rate including power losses through switchgear and controls associated with powering and controlling the fans (W)

P_{ef} is the total fan power of all exhaust air fans at the design air flow rate including power losses through switchgear and controls associated with powering and controlling the fans (W) and

q is the design air flow rate through the system, which should be the greater of either the supply or exhaust air flow (litre/s).

Specific fan power of an individual fan

The specific fan power of an individual fan, SFP_v, is defined as in Equation 12:

$$SFP_v = \frac{P_{mains}}{q_f}$$

Equation 12

where P_{mains} is the power supplied to the fan (W) and q_f is the airflow rate through the fan (litre/s).

10.3 Minimum provisions for air handling units in new and existing buildings

In order to comply with ADL2A and ADL2B, air handling units in new and existing buildings should meet the following minimum provisions:

a. An air handling system should be capable of achieving a specific fan power at 25% of design flow rate no greater than that achieved at 100% design flow rate; and

b. In order to aid commissioning and to provide flexibility for future changes of use, reasonable provision would be to equip with variable speed drives those fans that are rated at more than 1100W and which form part of the environmental control system(s), including smoke control fans used for control of overheating. *The provision is not applicable to smoke control fans and similar ventilation systems only used in abnormal circumstances*; and

c. In order to limit air leakage, ventilation ductwork should be made and assembled so as to be reasonably airtight. One way of achieving this would be to comply with the specifications given in HVCA DW144 ('Specifications for sheet metal ductwork', DW144, HVCA, 1998). Membership of the HVCA specialist ductwork group or the Association of Ductwork Contractors and Allied Services is one way of demonstrating suitable qualifications.

d. The air distribution system should be installed to meet a specific fan power that does not exceed the values given in Table 35 for new buildings and in Table 36 for existing buildings.

New buildings

Where fan systems are installed to either provide ventilation or air circulation, reasonable provision would be to install air distribution systems whose specific fan power at the design air flow rate is no worse than the values in Table 35.

Table 35 Limiting specific fan powers, W/(litre/s) in new buildings

System type	SFP, W/(litre/s)
Central mechanical ventilation including heating, cooling and heat recovery	2.5
Central mechanical ventilation with heating and cooling	2.0
All other central systems	1.8
Local ventilation only units within the local area, such as window/wall/roof units, serving one room or area	0.5
Local ventilation only units remote from the area such as ceiling void or roof mounted units, serving one room or area*	1.2
Other local units, e.g. fan coil units (rating weighted average**)	0.8

Notes:
 *This also includes fan assisted terminal VAV units where the primary air and cooling is provided by central plant.
**The rating weighted average is calculated by the following formula

$$\frac{P_{mains,1} .SFP_1 + P_{mains,2} .SFP_2 + P_{mains,3} .SFP_3 + \ldots}{P_{mains,1} + P_{mains,2} + P_{mains,3} + \ldots}$$

Work in existing buildings

Where the work involves the provision of a controlled service, reasonable provision would be to provide new services that meet reasonable standards of energy efficiency. Under such circumstances whenever air handling plant is provided or replaced, reasonable provision would be to provide installations whose specific fan power at the design flow rate is no worse than the values in Table 36.

Table 36 Limiting specific fan powers, W/(litre/s) in existing buildings

System type	SFP, W/(litre/s)
Central mechanical ventilation including heating, cooling and heat recovery	3.0
Central mechanical ventilation with heating and cooling	2.5
All other central systems	2.0
Local ventilation only units within the local area, such as window/wall/roof units, serving one room or area	0.5
Local ventilation only units remote from the area such as ceiling void or roof mounted units, serving one room or area*	1.5
Other local units e.g. fan coil units (rating weighted average**)	0.8

Notes:
 *This also includes fan assisted terminal VAV units where the primary air and cooling is provided by central plant.
**The rating weighted average is calculated by the following formula

$$\frac{P_{mains,1} . SFP_1 + P_{mains,2} . SFP_2 + P_{mains,3} . SFP_3 + \ldots}{P_{mains,1} + P_{mains,2} + P_{mains,3} + \ldots}$$

Section 11 Pipework and duct insulation

This section outlines the minimum provisions needed to comply with Part L when insulating pipework and ducting serving space heating, hot water and cooling systems in new build and in existing buildings.

11.1 Introduction

The insulation of pipework and ducting is essential to minimise heat losses for heated systems and heat gains for cooled systems. For cooled systems, it is also important to ensure that the risk of condensation is adequately controlled; this is however not within the scope of the guidance given in this section. The 'TIMSA HVAC Guide for achieving compliance with Part L of the Building Regulations' gives additional information and guidance on controlling condensation and all other provisions required for compliance with Part L.

11.2 Scope of the guidance

The guidance in this section applies to the insulation of pipes and ductwork serving space heating, hot water and cooling systems as follows:

- Pipes – direct hot water pipework, low, medium and high temperature heating pipework and cooled pipework

- Ducts – heated ductwork, cooled ductwork and dual-purpose heated and cooled ductwork

11.3 Minimum provisions for insulation of pipes and ducts in new and existing buildings

In order to comply with ADL2A and ADL2B in new and existing buildings the following minimum provisions for insulation of pipes and ducts serving heating and cooling systems must be met:

a. **Direct hot water and heating pipework** – pipework serving space heating and hot water systems should be insulated in all areas outside of the heated building envelope. In addition, pipes should be insulated in all voids within the building envelope and within spaces which will normally be heated if there is a possibility that those spaces might be maintained at temperatures different to those maintained in other zones. The guiding principles are that control should be maximised and that heat loss from uninsulated pipes should only be permitted where the heat can be demonstrated as 'always useful'. In order to demonstrate compliance the maximum permissible heat losses for different pipe sizes and temperatures, as given in Table 37, should not be exceeded.

b. **Cooled pipework** – cooled pipework should be insulated along its whole length in order to provide the necessary means of limiting heat gain. Control should be maximised and heat gain to uninsulated pipes should only be permitted where the proportion of the cooling load relating to distribution pipework is proven to be less than 5% of total load. In order to demonstrate compliance, the maximum permissible heat gain for different pipe sizes and temperatures, as given in Table 38, should not be exceeded[29]. Additional provision for the control of condensation may need to be made as detailed in the TIMSA HVAC Guide.

c. **Hot and cooled ducting** – ducting should be insulated along its whole length in order to provide the necessary means of limiting heat gains and/or heat losses from ducts. Where ducting may be used for both heating and cooling duties at different periods during its lifecycle, the provisions for chilled ducting should be adopted, since these are the most onerous. Table 39 indicates the maximum heat loss/gain per unit area required to meet these provisions (heat gains are shown as negative values). As with pipes, additional insulation may be required to provide adequate condensation control. Further details regarding these specific requirements are given in the TIMSA HVAC Guide.

---

29   It is recommended that requirements for the control of condensation are assessed using the TIMSA HVAC guide when specifying a system.

Table 37 Maximum permissible heat loss (W/m) for direct hot water and heating pipes

Outside pipe diameter (mm)	Maximum permissible heat loss (W/m)			
	Hot water[1]	Low temp. heating[2]	Medium temp. heating[3]	High temp. heating[4]
		≤ 95°C	96°C–120°C	121°C–150°C
17.2	6.60	8.90	13.34	17.92
21.3	7.13	9.28	13.56	18.32
26.9	7.83	10.06	13.83	18.70
33.7	8.62	11.07	14.39	19.02
42.4	9.72	12.30	15.66	19.25
48.3	10.21	12.94	16.67	20.17
60.3	11.57	14.45	18.25	21.96
76.1	13.09	16.35	20.42	24.21
88.9	14.58	17.91	22.09	25.99
114.3	17.20	20.77	25.31	29.32
139.7	19.65	23.71	28.23	32.47
168.3	22.31	26.89	31.61	36.04
219.1	27.52	32.54	37.66	42.16
273.0 & above	32.40	38.83	43.72	48.48

Notes 1, 2, 3, 4: To ensure compliance with maximum permissible heat loss criteria, proposed insulation thicknesses should be calculated according to BS EN ISO 12241 using standardised assumptions:
[1] Horizontal pipe at 60°C in still air at 15°C
[2] Horizontal pipe at 75°C in still air at 15°C
[3] Horizontal pipe at 100°C in still air at 15°C
[4] Horizontal pipe at 125°C in still air at 15°C

Table 38 Maximum permissible heat gain for cooled water supplies

Outside diameter of steel pipe on which insulation has been based	Maximum permissible heat gain (W/m)		
	Temperature of contents (°C)		
mm	>10[5]	4.9 to 10.0[6]	0 to 4.9[7]
17.2	2.48	2.97	3.47
21.3	2.72	3.27	3.81
26.9	3.05	3.58	4.18
33.7	3.41	4.01	4.60
42.4	3.86	4.53	5.11
48.3	4.11	4.82	5.45
60.3	4.78	5.48	6.17
76.1	5.51	6.30	6.70
88.9	6.17	6.90	7.77
114.3	7.28	8.31	9.15
139.7	8.52	9.49	10.45
168.3	9.89	10.97	11.86
219.1	12.27	13.57	14.61
273.0 and above	14.74	16.28	17.48

Note: Thicknesses given are calculated specifically against the criteria noted in the table. Adopting these thicknesses may not necessarily satisfy other design requirements such as control of condensation.

[5, 6, 7] To ensure compliance with maximum permissible heat gain criteria, proposed insulation thicknesses should be calculated according to BS EN ISO 12241 using standardised assumptions:
[5] Horizontal pipe at 10°C in still air at 25°C
[6] Horizontal pipe at 5°C in still air at 25°C
[7] Horizontal pipe at 0°C in still air at 25°C

Table 39 Maximum permissible heat gain/loss for insulated ducts used to carry cooled air (including those heated ducts used periodically for cooled air)

	Heated duct[8]	Dual purpose[9]	Cooled duct[10]
Maximum permissible heat transfer (W/m²)	16.34	-6.45	-6.45

[8, 9, 10] To ensure compliance with maximum permissible heat transfer criteria, proposed insulation thicknesses should be calculated according to BS EN ISO 12241 using standardised assumptions:
[8] Horizontal duct at 35°C, with 600mm vertical sidewall in still air at 15°C
[9] Horizontal duct at 13°C, with 600mm vertical sidewall in still air at 25°C
[10] Horizontal duct at 13°C, with 600mm vertical sidewall in still air at 25°C

Section 12 Compliance checklist and data input into the National Calculation Methodology tool

The compliance checklist is included in Appendix 2 of this guide. This table lists all the space heating technologies for primary heating, hot water systems, cooling systems and air distribution systems within the scope of the Non-domestic Heating, Cooling and Ventilation Compliance Guide and summarises the main compliance requirements. The checklist does not cover the minimum provisions for insulation of pipes and ducts serving heating or cooling systems as given in Section 11 of this guide.

The purpose of the compliance checklist is twofold. The checklist can be used:

- By Building Control Officers as a simple means of checking the compliance of a heating, comfort cooling or hot water system;

- By users of the approved building energy performance calculation tools to determine the correct parameters for compliance of heating, comfort cooling or hot water systems to input into the tool. As it is not possible to cover all possible approved calculation tools, this compliance checklist focuses on the data inputs for the SBEM calculation tool.

Note that other approved calculation tools may be used and the data required are made transparent in each of the technology-specific sections. For example, all of the heating efficiency credits are provided for users of other approved calculation tools to incorporate in their models.

The SBEM calculation tool and the accompanying user guide are available from the website (www.ncm.bre.co.uk). Section 6 of the user guide (version 1.0.0) explains how to input data into SBEM relating to Building Services.

How to use the compliance checklist

The compliance checklist is a table summarising the key criteria for compliance with the minimum provisions of the Building Regulations, Part L for heating, hot water, cooling and ventilation systems as detailed in this guide. It is important that building services designers consult individual sections of this guide as using the compliance checklist alone will not enable a full appreciation of the minimum provisions for compliance with Part L.

The checklist is divided into six columns as follows:

Column 1: Technology

This column lists all the space heating systems for primary heating, DHW systems, cooling and air distribution systems covered in the Non-domestic Heating, Cooling and Ventilation Compliance Guide.

Column 2: Efficiency check

This column shows the minimum acceptable efficiency for each type of heating or cooling system and the maximum permissible specific fan power for air distribution systems. These minimum (or, for fans, maximum) acceptable efficiency values are designated Value A1 to Value A11. The actual design values can be entered in the adjacent sub-column – the design values are designated Value B1 to Value B11. The final sub-column allows a record that the appropriate check has been made.

Column 3: Minimum controls package check

This column displays all the control measures which should be specified as part of the minimum controls package. An entry can be made in the adjacent sub-column to indicate that the check has been made.

Column 4: Additional controls – heating efficiency credits check

This column shows all the measures that are additional to the minimum controls package, for which heating efficiency credits can be gained. The values assigned to each additional measure can be checked and summed to obtain the total Heating Efficiency Credits. The values for the total heating efficiency credits are designated value C2 to value C5, and C7 to C8.

Note that heating efficiency credits are not defined for all types of technologies. In some cases it may be acceptable for values C2 or C3, C4, etc. to be zero. This would be the case if the value of the heat generator seasonal efficiency meets or exceeds the minimum acceptable Effective Heat Generating Seasonal Efficiency as defined in each technology-specific section of this guide.

Column 5: Summary compliance check

This column describes the key compliance requirements and prompts the user for additional checks where these are not already covered in columns 2, 3 and 4.

Column 6: Data input to NCM tool (SBEM) check

This column indicates the efficiency value that should be entered in the approved calculation tools. It also indicates the name of the field in SBEM in which the value should be entered, as in some cases the terminology used in SBEM may be different to that used in this guide.

Note that the compliance checklist does not cover data inputs related to building services which may be required by SBEM, other than those which are defined in this Non-domestic Heating, Cooling and Ventilation Compliance Guide as a minimum provision for compliance with Part L.

Section 13 Glossary

Approved Document L2A	ADL2A	Approved Document L2A gives guidance on how to satisfy Part L (Conservation of fuel and power in new buildings other than dwellings – 2006 edition) of the Building Regulations in common situations. Effective from 6 April 2006.
Approved Document L2B	ADL2B	Approved Document L2B gives guidance on how to satisfy Part L (Conservation of fuel and power in existing buildings other than dwellings – 2006 edition) of the Building Regulations in common situations for work in non-domestic buildings. Effective from 6 April 2006.
The Building Regulations		Statutory Instrument 2000 No. 2531. The Building Regulations ensure the health and safety of people in and around buildings by providing functional requirements for building design and construction.
Office of the Deputy Prime Minister	ODPM	The government department responsible for producing and revising The Building Regulations. On 5th May 2006 the responsibilities of the ODPM passed to the Department for Communities and Local Government (DCLG).
Non-domestic Heating, Cooling and Ventilation Compliance Guide		This second-tier document in support of Approved Documents L2A and L2B setting out the minimum standards of provision that meet the requirements of Part L for conventional space heating, hot water and cooling systems provided in new build other than dwellings and for work in existing buildings other than dwellings.
National Calculation Methodology	NCM	The National Calculation Methodology defines the procedure for demonstrating compliance with the Building Regulations for buildings other than dwellings. This involves calculating the annual energy use for a proposed building and comparing it with the energy use of a comparable 'notional' building. The NCM comprises the underlying method plus the standard data sets. The NCM can be implemented through accredited simulation software or in SBEM.
Simplified Building Energy Model	SBEM	A simplified tool underpinned by the National Calculation Methodology and based on a set of CEN standards which allows the calculation of annual energy use for a proposed building in order to demonstrate compliance with the Building Regulations for buildings other than dwellings.
Accredited NCM tool		A tool or model (such as SBEM) which is underpinned by the National Calculation Methodology which allows the calculation of annual energy use for a proposed building in order to demonstrate compliance with the Building Regulations for buildings other than dwellings.
European Committee for Standardization	CEN	CEN produces standards (often at the request of industry or at the request of the European Commission in order to implement European legislation). Harmonised CEN standards ensure consistent standards for products which may be manufactured, sold and installed across the EC.
Energy performance rating		In this document this refers to the annual energy use predicted for the building using the National Calculation Methodology.

Appendix 1: Conversion factors

The conversion factors in Table 40 can be used to convert efficiencies based on calorific value from net to gross and gross to net:

- To convert from net efficiency to gross, multiply by the factor for the appropriate fuel.
  As an example take a boiler at 80% net efficiency firing LPG.
  To convert to gross = 80 × 0.921 = 73.68%.

- To convert from gross efficiency to net, divide by the factor for the appropriate fuel.
  As an example take a boiler at 73.68% gross efficiency firing LPG.
  To convert to net = 73.68 ÷ 0.921 = 80.0%.

Table 40 Factors for converting efficiencies[30]

Fuel type	Conversion factor
Natural gas	0.901
Liquefied petroleum gas (LPG)	0.921
Oil	0.937

---

[30] Conversion factors are derived from The Government's Standard Assessment Procedure for Energy Rating of Dwellings 2005 edition (Table E.3 in Appendix E).

Appendix 2: Compliance checklist

Technology (1)	Efficiency Check (2)	Minimum Controls Package Check (3)	Additional controls – Heating Efficiency Credit Check (4)	Summary Compliance Check (5)	Data Input to NCM Tool (SBEM) Check (6)
Primary space heating system	Required Minimum Heat Generator Seasonal Efficiency (based on Gross Calorific Value)	Design Heat Generator Seasonal Efficiency for proposed building or existing dwelling **ENTER DESIGN VALUE**	Check – Design Heat Generator Seasonal Efficiency ≥ Required minimum efficiency **ENTER YES/NO**	Check that the controls/measures listed here, where adopted, are allocated the correct Heating Efficiency Credits and are summed correctly (if applicable)		Check value and field for SBEM

Boilers in new build

Technology	Required Minimum Boiler Seasonal Efficiency (based on Gross Calorific Value)	Design Boiler Seasonal Efficiency (weighted for part load) for proposed heating system	Check – Design Boiler Seasonal Efficiency (weighted for load profile) ≥ Required Boiler Seasonal Efficiency	Check ALL the controls listed here are specified as part of the Minimum Controls Package	Optional controls or other measures	Heating Plant Efficiency Credit (% points)	Summary Compliance Check	Data Input to NCM Tool
	▼ VALUE A1 ▼	▼ VALUE B1 ▼		Boiler plant size – design size:			1. Value B1 is no less than 84%	VALUE B1
				All boiler sizes **Package A:**			2. Boiler Seasonal Efficiency of each boiler in a multi-boiler system is not less than 80%	
Natural gas	**Single boiler system** – 0.84 **Multiple-boiler system** – 0.80 for any individual boiler and 0.84 for the overall multi-boiler system			Timing and temperature demand control – zone specific where the building floor area is > 150m² Y / N			3. Overall Boiler Seasonal Efficiency of multi-boiler system is no less than 84%	
				Weather compensation (except where constant temperature supply is needed) Y / N			4. All controls in Minimum Controls Package specified	
				100kw to 500kW **Package A above PLUS Package B**				
				Optimal start/stop control Y / N				
LPG	**Single boiler system** – 0.84 **Multiple-boiler system** – 0.80 for any individual boiler and 0.84 for the overall multi-boiler system			Night set back OR frost protection Y / N	Heating Efficiency Credits not applicable to boilers in new build			
				Two stage firing facility OR multiple boilers Y / N				
				Measures to limit heat loss from non-firing modules Y / N				
				Sequence controls – for multiple boilers only Y / N				
				> 500kW **Package A & B above PLUS C**				
Oil	**Single boiler system** – 0.84 **Multiple-boiler system** – 0.80 for any individual boiler and 0.84 for the overall multi-boiler system			For each gas boiler – fully modulating burner controls Y / N				This value should be entered in the field that is labelled in SBEM as the 'Generator Seasonal Efficiency'
				For each boiler – multi-stage burner controls Y / N				

Boilers in existing buildings

Technology (1)	Efficiency Check (2)			Minimum Controls Package Check (3)	Additional controls – Heating Efficiency Credit Check (4)		Summary Compliance Check (5)	Data Input to NCM Tool (SBEM) Check (6)
Primary space heating system	Required Minimum Heat Generator Seasonal Efficiency (based on Gross Calorific Value)	Design Heat Generator Seasonal Efficiency for proposed building or existing dwelling ENTER DESIGN VALUE	Check – Design Heat Generator Seasonal Efficiency ≥ Required minimum efficiency ENTER YES/NO	Check ALL the controls listed here are specified as part of the Minimum Controls Package	Check that the controls/measures listed here, where adopted, are allocated the correct Heating Efficiency Credits and are summed correctly (if applicable)			Check value and field for SBEM
	Required Minimum Boiler Seasonal Efficiency (based on Gross Calorific Value)	Design Boiler Seasonal Efficiency (weighted for part load) for proposed heating system	Check – Design Boiler Seasonal Efficiency (weighted for load profile) ≥ Required Boiler Seasonal Efficiency		Optional controls or other measures	Heating Plant Efficiency Credit (% points)	1. Value B2 is no less than the relevant value A2	VALUE B2 + VALUE C2
	▼ VALUE A2 ▼	▼ VALUE B2 ▼					2. Value B2 + Value C2 is no less than the relevant value: Gas boilers: 0.84 LPG boilers: 0.85 Oil boilers: 0.86	
Natural gas	0.80			Zone-control where the building floor area is > 150m² – as a minimum on/off control for the zone — Y / N	Boiler oversize no more than 20%	2	3. All controls in Minimum Controls Package specified	
					Sequential control of multiple boilers	1		
					Monitoring and targeting	1	4. Heating Efficiency Credits for extra measures adopted are assigned correctly	
					Thermostatic radiator valves	1		
					Weather compensation with mixing valve (a)	1.5		
LPG	0.81			Room thermostat which controls through a diverter valve (diverter valve not needed for condensing boiler) — Y / N	Addition of Thermostatic Radiator Valves or temperature zone control to a) above or to b) or c) below for full building temp control	1		
					Room thermostat or sensor controlling boiler water temp in relation to heat load (b)	0.5		
					Direct-acting weather compensation (c)	2		
					Optimised start	1.5		
					Optimised stop	0.5		
					Optimised start/stop	2		
Oil	0.82			Time clock controls — Y / N	Full zoned time control	1		
					Full Building Management System	4		
					Decentralised heating system	1		
					Multiple boilers	1		
					TOTAL CREDITS	VALUE C2		

Technology (1)	Efficiency Check (2)						Minimum Controls Package Check (3)	Additional controls – Heating Efficiency Credit Check (4)		Summary Compliance Check (5)	Data Input to NCM Tool (SBEM) Check (6)
Primary space heating system	Required Minimum Heat Generator Seasonal Efficiency (based on Gross Calorific Value)	Design Heat Generator Seasonal Efficiency for proposed building or existing dwelling **ENTER DESIGN VALUE**	Check – Design Heat Generator Seasonal Efficiency ≥ Required minimum efficiency **ENTER YES/NO**				**Check ALL the controls listed here are specified as part of the Minimum Controls Package**	**Check that the controls/measures listed here, where adopted, are allocated the correct Heating Efficiency Credits and are summed correctly (if applicable)**			**Check value and field for SBEM**
				Required Minimum Thermal Efficiency (based on Gross Calorific Value)	Design Thermal Efficiency for proposed building heating system	Check – Design Thermal Efficiency ≥ Required Minimum Thermal Efficiency		Optional controls or other measures	Heating Plant Efficiency Credit (% points)		
Warm air				▼ **VALUE A3** ▼	▼ **VALUE B3** ▼					1. Value B3 is no less than the relevant value A3	**VALUE B3 + (VALUE C3)**
										2. Heating Efficiency Credits for extra measures, where adopted, are assigned correctly	**This value should be entered in the field that is labelled in SBEM as the 'Generator Seasonal Efficiency'**
Gas-fired forced convection heater without fan	0.80						Time Control — Y / N	Optimised shut down	1		
Fan assisted gas-fired forced convection	0.80						Space temperature control — Y / N	Hi/lo burners	2	3. All controls in Minimum Controls Package specified	
Direct gas-fired forced convection heater	0.90						Zone control – only for buildings with a floor area > 150m² — Y / N	Modulating burners	3		
Oil-fired forced convection	0.80							**TOTAL CREDITS**	**VALUE C3**		
Radiant				▼ **VALUE A4** ▼	▼ **VALUE B4** ▼					1. Value B4 is no less than the relevant value A4	**VALUE B4 + (VALUE C4)**
Luminous (unflued)	0.855									2. Heating Efficiency Credits for extra measures, where adopted, are assigned correctly	**This value should be entered in the field that is labelled in SBEM as the 'Generator Seasonal Efficiency'**
Non-luminous (unflued)	0.855						Time control — Y / N	Optimised shut down	1		
Non-luminous (flued)	0.738						Space temperature control with black bulb sensors — Y / N			3. All controls in Minimum Controls Package specified	
Multi-burner radiant heaters	0.800							Zone control	1		
								TOTAL CREDITS	**VALUE C4**		

(1)	(2)			(3)		(4)		(5)	(6)
Primary space heating system	Required Minimum Heat Generator Seasonal Efficiency (based on Gross Calorific Value)	Design Heat Generator Seasonal Efficiency for proposed building or existing dwelling ENTER DESIGN VALUE	Check – Design Heat Generator Seasonal Efficiency ≥ Required minimum efficiency ENTER YES/NO	Check ALL the controls listed here are specified as part of the Minimum Controls Package	Check – Minimum Controls Package specified ENTER YES OR NO	Check that the controls/measures listed here, where adopted, are allocated the correct Heating Efficiency Credits and are summed correctly (if applicable)	Heating Plant Efficiency Credit (% points)		Check value and field for SBEM

Heat Pump

	Required Minimum Heating CoP (at design condition)	Design Heating CoP (at design condition) for proposed heating system	Check – Design Heating CoP ≥ Required Minimum Heating CoP	Required controls for heat pumps	Check – Minimum Controls Package specified ENTER YES OR NO	Optional controls or other measures	Heating Plant Efficiency Credit (% points)	1. Value B5 is no less than the relevant value A5	VALUE B5 + (VALUE C5/100)
	▶ VALUE A5 ▶	▶ VALUE B5 ▶							
All types except absorption heat pumps and gas engine heat pumps	2.0			On/off zone control for buildings with floor area > 150m²	Y / N	< 20% oversizing	2		
				Time control	Y / N				
				Control of room temp if not provided externally OR control of water temp for Water or Ground to Water types	Y / N	Optimised stop	2		
				Control of outdoor fan operation	Y / N				
Absorption heat pumps	0.5			Defrost control (except water or ground to air)	Y / N	Full zone control	2		
				Control for secondary heating (if fitted, except Water or Ground to Water types)	Y / N	M&T	2		This value should be entered in the field that is labelled in SBEM as the 'Generator Seasonal Efficiency'
				External controls					
				Room thermostat (if not integral to heat pump) to regulate space temp and interlocked with heat pump unit operation	Y / N				
Gas engine driven heat pumps	1.0			Control of external water pump operation – Water or Ground to Air types only	Y / N				
				Control of internal/external water pump operation – Water or Ground to Water types only	Y / N	TOTAL CREDITS	VALUE C5		

CHP

	Required Minimum CHPQA Quality Index (CHPQA QI)	Design CHPQA Quality Index for proposed heating system	Check – CHPQA QI ≥ Required Minimum CHPQA QI	Required controls for heat pumps	Check – Minimum Controls Package specified ENTER YES OR NO	Optional controls or other measures	Heating Plant Efficiency Credit (% points)	1. Value B6 is no less than value A6	Proportion of annual heat demand (H) supplied from CHP, Overall efficiency (E), Heat to Power ratio (R)
	▶ VALUE A6 ▶	▶ VALUE B6 ▶						2. Metering of the hours run, the electricity generated and the fuel supplied to the CHP unit	
All types	105			Control system to ensure CHP unit is the lead heat generator	Y / N	Heating Efficiency Credits not applicable to CHP		3. Back-up boilers meet the minimum efficiency and control requirements for boilers in section 2 of the Non-Domestic Heating, Cooling and Ventilation Compliance Guide	

Primary space heating system

Technology (1)	Efficiency Check (2)			Minimum Controls Package Check (3)		Additional controls – Heating Efficiency Credit Check (4)		Summary Compliance Check (5)	Data Input to NCM Tool (SBEM) Check (6)
	Required Minimum Heat Generator Seasonal Efficiency (based on Gross Calorific Value)	Design Heat Generator Seasonal Efficiency for proposed building or existing dwelling **ENTER DESIGN VALUE**	Check – Design Heat Generator Seasonal Efficiency ≥ Required minimum efficiency **ENTER YES/NO**	Check ALL the controls listed here are specified as part of the Minimum Controls Package	Check – Minimum Controls Package specified **ENTER YES OR NO**	Check that the controls/measures listed here, where adopted, are allocated the correct Heating Efficiency Credits and are summed correctly (if applicable)	Heating Plant Efficiency Credit (% points)		Check value and field for SBEM
				Required controls for electric heating		Optional controls or other measures		1. All controls in Minimum Controls Package are specified OR a boiler management control system that meets all the specified zoning, time and temperature requirements	
Electric (primary) heating									
	▼ VALUE A7 ▼	▼ VALUE B7 ▼							For electric systems, 1.0 should be entered in the field that is labelled in SBEM as the 'Generator Seasonal Efficiency' (or leave the SBEM default value of 1.0)
Boiler	N/A (assumed to have 100% efficiency at the point of energy conversion)	N/A	N/A	Boiler temperature control (ability for flow temp control and modulating power input to primary water depending on space heating conditions)	Y / N	Heating Efficiency Credits not applicable to electric heating systems			
				Zoning (At least two zones with space temp control for buildings with floor area up to 150m². At least two space heating zones, each with separate time and temp control for buildings with floor area > 150m²)	Y / N				
				Temperature control of space heating – with i) Room thermostats or programmable room thermostats in all zones OR (ii) A room thermostat or programmable room thermostat in the main zone and individual radiator controls on all radiators in the other zones OR a combination of (i) and (ii) above	Y / N				
				Time control of space heating with (i) full programmer with separate timing to each circuit OR (ii) two or more separate timers providing timing control to each circuit OR (iii) programmable room thermostat(s) to the heating circuit(s), with separate timing of each circuit	Y / N				
Warm air	N/A (assumed to be 100% efficient)	N/A	N/A	Time switch/programmer and room stat OR programmable room thermostat	Y / N				
				Zone control using multiple heating zone programmers OR single multi-channel programmers	Y / N				

Domestic hot water systems

Technology (1)	Efficiency Check (2)		Minimum Controls Package Check (3)		Additional controls – Heating Efficiency Credit Check (4)		Summary Compliance Check (5)	Data Input to NCM Tool (SBEM) Check (6)
	Required Minimum Thermal Efficiencies (based on Gross Calorific Value)	Design Thermal Efficiency (based on gross CV) for proposed hot water system	Check – Design Thermal Efficiency ≥ Required Minimum Thermal Efficiency / Required controls for DHW systems	Check – Minimum Controls Package specified ENTER YES OR NO	Optional controls or other measures	Heating Plant Efficiency Credit (% points)	1. Value B8 is no less than value A8. / 2. Heating Efficiency Credits for extra measures, where adopted, are assigned correctly. / 3. All controls in Minimum Controls Package specified	VALUE B8 + (VALUE C8)
	▼ VALUE A8 ▼	▼ VALUE B8 ▼						
Gas and Oil-fired systems								
Direct-fired					Decentralisation (not applicable to systems in new buildings)	2		
Natural gas	0.73		Automatic thermostat control	Y / N				
LPG-fired	0.74		Time control	Y / N	Confirm correct size of unit using manufacturer's technical help lines or manufacturer's sizing software	2		
Oil-fired	0.75							
Indirect-fired (dedicated hot water boiler)			Automatic thermostat control	Y / N				
Natural gas	0.80		High limit thermostat (thermal cut-out)	Y / N	Integral combustion circuit shut-off device – direct fired systems only	1		
LPG-fired	0.81		Time control	Y / N				
Oil-fired	0.82				Fully automatic ignition controls – direct fired systems only	0.5		
Electric DHW heaters								
Electric systems			Controls for electric DHW	Check – Minimum Controls Package specified ENTER YES OR NO				
Point of use	N/A (assumed to have 100% efficiency at the point of energy conversion)	N/A	Automatic thermostat control – Required for all electric heater types except instantaneous	Y / N				
			High limit thermostat (thermal cut-out) – Required for all electric heater types except instantaneous	Y / N				
Local electrically heated	N/A (assumed to have 100% efficiency at the point of energy conversion)	N/A	Manual re-set in the event of an over-temperature trip – Required for all electric heater types except instantaneous	Y / N				
Centralised electrically heated	N/A (assumed to have 100% efficiency at the point of energy conversion)	N/A	A 7-day time-clock (or BMS interface). Facility to boost the temperature using on-peak electricity – Required only for local and centralised electrically heated water heaters	Y / N	TOTAL CREDITS	VALUE C8		
Instantaneous electrically heated	N/A (assumed to have 100% efficiency at the point of energy conversion)		High limit thermostat (thermal cut-out) – Required only for instantaneous heaters	Y / N				
			Flow sensor – Required only for instantaneous heaters	Y / N				

Technology (1)	Efficiency Check (2)		Minimum Controls Package Check (3)		Additional controls – Heating Efficiency Credit Check (4)	Summary Compliance Check (5)	Data Input to NCM Tool (SBEM) Check (6)
Comfort cooling systems	Required Minimum Energy Efficiency Ratio (EER)	Seasonal Energy Efficiency Ratio (SEER) for proposed cooling system with part load data but unknown load profile – check ≥ minimum EER	Design SEER for proposed cooling system with part load data and in an office or with known load profile – check ≥ minimum EER	Check – Minimum Controls Package specified **ENTER YES OR NO**	N/A	1. Value B9 is no less than relevant value A9 2. All controls in Minimum Controls Package specified	**VALUE B9**
Cooling							
Packaged air conditioners	Single duct 1.8 Other types 2.2 ▼ VALUE A9 ▼	▼ VALUE B9 ▼		**Cooling plant**			This value should be entered in the field that is labelled in SBEM as the *'Generator Seasonal EER'*
Split and multi-split air-conditioners (including VRF)	2.4			Controls on multiple-cooling modules	Y / N		
Vapour compression cycle chillers – water cooled	3.4			**Cooling system**			
Vapour compression cycle chillers – air cooled	2.25			Integral or remote controls for time and temperature control of each terminal cooling unit	Y / N		
Water loop heat pump	3.2						
Absorption cycle chillers	0.5						
Gas fired Variable Refrigerant Flow (VRF)	0.5			Interlock to prevent simultaneous heating and cooling in any zone	Y / N		

Air distribution systems

Technology (1)	Efficiency Check (2) Maximum permissible specific fan power (Watts/(litres/s))	Efficiency Check (2) Design specific fan power (Watts/litres/s) for proposed air distribution system	Efficiency Check (2) Check – Design Specific Fan Power ≤ Maximum permissible SFP	Minimum Controls Package Check (3)	Additional controls – Heating Efficiency Credit Check (4)	Summary Compliance Check (5)	Data Input to NCM Tool (SBEM) Check (6)
New buildings	▼ VALUE A10 ▼	▼ VALUE B10 ▼				1. For new buildings, Value B10 is no less than relevant value A10 OR For existing buildings, Value B11 is no less than Value A11	
Central mechanical ventilation including heating, cooling and heat recovery	2.5			N/A	N/A	2. The air handling system is capable of achieving a specific fan power at 25% of design flow rate no greater than that achieved at 100% design flow rate	Value B10 for new buildings
Central mechanical ventilation with heating and cooling	2						This value should be entered in the field that is labelled in SBEM as the 'SFP (specific fan power) for the system' under the 'System Adjustment' tab
All other central systems	1.8						
Local ventilation only units within the local area, such as window/wall/roof units, serving one room or area	0.5					3. Fans rated >1100W *and which form part* of the environmental control systems (including smoke control fans used for control of overheating) are equipped with Variable Speed Drives	
Local ventilation only units remote from the area such as ceiling void or roof mounted units, serving one room or area. This also includes fan assisted terminal VAV units where the primary air and cooling is provided by central plant	1.2					4. Ventilation ductwork complies with airtightness requirements (HVCA DW144 specification or membership of HVCA specialist ductwork group OR Association of Ductwork Contractors and Allied Services)	
Other local units e.g. fan coil units (rating weighted average)	0.8						
Existing buildings	▼ VALUE A11 ▼	▼ VALUE B11 ▼					Value B11 for existing buildings
Central mechanical ventilation including heating, cooling and heat recovery	3.0			N/A	N/A		
Central mechanical ventilation with heating and cooling	2.5						
All other central systems	2						
Local ventilation only units within the local area, such as window/wall/roof units, serving one room or area	0.5						
Local ventilation only units remote from the area such as ceiling void or roof mounted units, serving one room or area	1.5						
Other local units e.g. fan coil units (rating weighted average)	0.8						